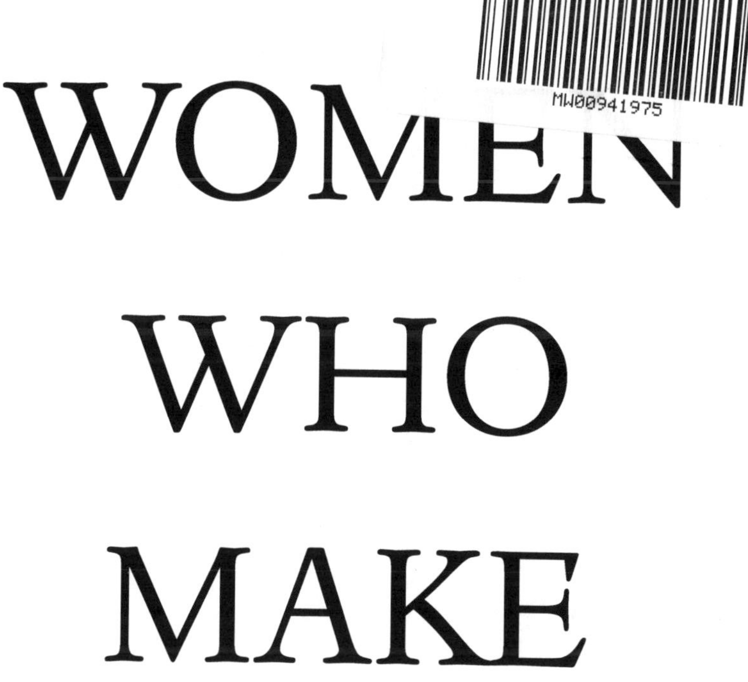

WOMEN WHO MAKE

INSPIRING STORIES OF WOMEN WHO FOUND FULFILLING STEM CAREERS IN MANUFACTURING MAKING THINGS WITH MEANING

Bonita Richter, MBA

WOMEN WHO MAKE

TYPESET BY PROFIT STRATEGIES, PALATINE, ILLINOIS

Cover design by David Miles/Reedsy Ltd.

Printed in the U.S.A.

To order this title, please call 847.989.0513.

For information, contact www.profit-strategies.com/contact.

ISBN: 978-0-578-59125-4

ISBN: 978-0-578-59126-1

This book is dedicated to my father, Gerald Eugene Troutman, who is my inspiration.

Contents

Introduction

Do you like creating and making things?

Does the WWII icon, Rosie the Riveter, and her "*We Can Do It!*" message inspire you?

Do you want to work with smart people who are on the leading edge of innovation?

Does the sound of whirring, fast-spinning, high-tech machinery secretly excite you?

Do you want a well-paying job that leads to a lifelong career path?

If you answered yes to any of these questions, then a career in manufacturing and other STEM-related jobs (i.e., jobs related to science, technology, engineering, and math) may be right for you.

But how do you know for sure?

That's what this book is all about: to help you learn more about manufacturing through real-life stories of women who are working, succeeding, and creating fulfilling lives in the industry.

They know through first-hand experience that manufacturing is a viable career path for women, and they want more women to join them. Through their stories, they chip away at the negative stereotypes and common misconceptions about manufacturing.

You undoubtedly have many questions about manufacturing:

- What kinds of careers and jobs are available in manufacturing?
- Will I be working on a factory line?
- Are office jobs the only ones open to women?
- What is it like to work in manufacturing?
- Are women welcome?
- Is there a path for career growth?
- What is the income potential?

You'll find the answers to all of these questions and more in the pages of this book.

Women Who are Changing the Future of Manufacturing

Stories change lives. They help us translate the information we hear into meaning. The women in this book have shared their personal, life experiences that have led them to where they are now in their careers—women who are enjoying working in, and owning companies in, the manufacturing industry. Their jobs have allowed them to live well, be who they are, and enjoy life.

Women are rising to the top of the manufacturing industry and are inspiring the women of the next generation to pursue careers in the industry and find out what it offers: economic empowerment, and a rewarding and fulfilling career with limitless opportunity for growth.

For this book, I interviewed sixteen women in the Chicago, Illinois region—the second-largest hub of manufacturing activity in the United States[1]—who work at various jobs in manufacturing. They range from CEOs, and presidents who are leading their own companies, to a young woman who is an apprentice machine operator. I also interviewed women in high-responsibility positions—a quality control inspector and the head of purchasing, and various administrative positions. Some of these women have been part of the manufacturing industry for decades. Others are newcomers—women who have, at the time of this writing, only worked in the manufacturing industry for a few short years. This book is not merely stories about 'women in manufacturing.' It is about women who are *leaders,* and way-showers to show other women how to move onto their path to express their interests, talents, and gifts to the world in a larger way through a STEM-related career.

Their stories can serve to inform and inspire other women to join them in the ranks of manufacturing, because these women have experienced exciting and financially rewarding careers. They each told me there is, unequivocally, a massive opportunity for career advancement and growth for women in the manufacturing industry. They know that their stories are one of the most potent assets they have when it comes to teaching what they know, and that their knowledge is a tremendous gift they can pass on to others, and they are excited to share their stories with you.

Because I have structured this book in the interview style, you will get to hear each woman's own voice and read her own words. Through these women's stories, you will get to know them, learn from them, and have a sense of what they felt through the telling of their stories.

I asked each woman what advice she would give to a young woman (and to her parents) who is contemplating a career in manufacturing. They each answered this question enthusiastically and shared their thoughts and ideas about the fantastic career opportunities available.

You will gain a greater understanding of the world of a manufacturing career through their experiences. I hope, through their stories and all that you learn within this book, that you (and your parents) will be inspired to explore manufacturing as a viable career choice for yourself.

Please note: one thing this book is not is a scientific research study about women in manufacturing. It is a collection of interviews given by successful women working in manufacturing who want more women to join them in the industry.

Manufacturing is the backbone of America. It strengthens our country's economy and provides jobs that have high potential for career growth and advancement. Getting more women into manufacturing and other STEM-related fields provides a tremendous benefit for women, because these jobs often pay more than other types of jobs—and they're in high demand by employers. With advances in innovation and technology, manufacturing is creating exciting opportunities and well-paid careers for women (and men) of all ages.

I hope you will be inspired, through seeing the industry through these women's eyes, to explore manufacturing and other STEM fields as a potential career path. If some of what you have just read might sound familiar to you, I'm here to tell you that there is so much more to explore, and to learn, about the plethora of career opportunities available to you to pursue.

How to Use This Book

Part 1—Will define what manufacturing is and what STEM is, will convey how vital manufacturing is to the U.S. economy, and provide examples of typical jobs in the industry.

Part 2—Here's where you'll find each woman's story. You can read them in any order you prefer. At the end of each interview, you will see a "Career Activities" section, which will have questions and exercises to help you to dive deeper into the process of pondering if a career in manufacturing or a STEM-related field is right for you.

Part 3—Includes helpful resources and recommended books that will help lead you in the right direction of exploring and learning more about manufacturing and STEM.

Let this book serve your exploration and discovery process. Take this book with you so you can refer to it whenever you want to. Go ahead and take notes in the margins. Underline words. Put exclamation points next to lines that stand out to you! Draw diagrams. Make the information come alive for you. *Use this book* to help you learn and explore, and let it help to inspire you to find out what a career in manufacturing can offer you!

Author's note: In the interviews, the women's voices have been rendered authentically. Text in brackets serves to add in any missing words, clarify a pronoun, or the like. I've made additions within parenthesis (and italicized text) to clarify and/or flesh out topics as needed. My questions are in bold text, with their answers to my questions following.

PART 1:
MAKING THINGS

What are Manufacturing and STEM, Anyway?

Innovating and Making Things

In the plainest terms, manufacturing means starting with raw material and processing it by taking it through a series of steps to make it into something else as an end product. A slat of metal is machined to become a high-strength part in an aircraft engine. Tomatoes get steamed, mashed, seasoned, and made into a delicious spaghetti sauce. Water and essential oils are mixed to create a lovely scented perfume. There are many types of manufacturing companies that use many different methods to turn raw materials into things we can use in our daily lives.

Some manufacturers make handcrafted products by primarily using basic tools. Examples of things made by hand, using basic tools and methods of manufacturing, can range from hand-tooled leather shoes to hand-dipped chocolate candy. Even cars can be assembled by hand, such as the luxury car brand Rolls Royce. Objects made by hand take more time and are costlier to make. Almost anything you buy that is "made by hand" will cost more money than if it is machine-made.

Other manufacturers make machine-made products using mechanized and automated machinery that make things faster, in larger quantities, and cost less money to make. This kind of manufacturing is sophisticated and does not require as much manual handling of materials as basic manufacturing methods. Instead, these manufacturers use computers, precision-electronic equipment, and high-tech processing methods that require skilled labor and expensive machines.

This latter style of manufacturing is what we will talk about in this book: manufacturing that is highly technical, automated, and requires specially trained and skilled workers.

Today's manufacturing jobs are not the dirty jobs your parents and grandparents remember. The reason for this change came from innovation and advancements in technology used in manufacturing, as well as environmental groups and governments pushing and regulating to decrease waste, control pollution, and create a cleaner environment

Manufacturing is the backbone of America because it strengthens our country's economy by creating goods that U.S. companies can trade globally. By increasing productivity through innovation and automation, the amount of goods that can be produced is increased, which fuels Gross Domestic Product (or GDP—the total value of goods and services produced in the U.S. in one year), a measure of economic growth.

Manufacturing also creates middle-class jobs with good-paying wages. Factor in, too, that the U.S. has the power to create wealth through manufacturing, as well as help keep the citizens of our country safe by having the ability to produce military equipment, which can have a deterrent effect when it comes to the possibility of a hostile nation challenging us to war.[2]

About STEM . . .

Many people are talking about the benefits of a STEM education. But what is STEM and why is it important? STEM is the acronym for the subjects of science, technology, engineering, and math. These subjects are indelibly linked to the advanced technologies used in manufacturing.

Most of the time when you hear STEM being talked or written about, the author or speaker is referring to getting a college degree in one of these four fields. But did you know that there are many subcategories for each of the main categories of STEM? Manufacturing is one of those subcategories.

Here are some examples of how STEM subjects link to manufacturing:

- **Science:** Understanding the properties of different materials and chemicals is essential for successfully processing raw products. You have to know which ones are the best to use for particular applications. For example, aluminum, a strong, lightweight metal that is corrosion-resistant, is the metal chosen for making the bodies of aircrafts, rather than steel, which is a weighty metal that rusts easily.

- **Technology:** Advanced technologies are applied in all types of manufacturing—from automated electronic machine tools, to robotics, to computer programs. Computer programs instruct the automated machinery and equipment, such as machine tools, to perform specific processes to make different products.

- **Engineering:** The most common engineering disciplines in the manufacturing industry are mechanical, industrial, and chemical engineering. Engineers invent, design, and also help instruct others on how to build the products they, and others, have designed.

- **Math:** Algebra, trigonometry, geometry, and calculus all are used to design products and calculate the correct numerical values and thresholds for all different kinds of manufacturing parameters.

Many STEM advocates and policymakers believe that these subjects form the foundation for the 21st-century skills needed for jobs in the future because innovation and economic growth are fostered in the STEM fields. Manufacturing is one of these job pathways because science, technology, engineering, and math are applied every single day to design and make parts that go into products and technology that we all use in our daily lives.

Wherever you are sitting or standing right now, take a moment and look at the things around you. Everything you see that is man-made was manufactured: automobiles, smartphones, TVs, furniture, packaged food products, makeup and beauty products, aircraft, books; the list goes on and on and is almost endless.

It is important to note that some manufacturing and STEM jobs are higher paying than others.[3] For example, a person who goes to college and earns a bachelor's degree in mechanical engineering will receive a higher income than someone who chooses to get vocational-technical job training to be a machinist. There are ample opportunities for job and career growth in manufacturing, as you will see when you read the women's stories, and my personal story, in this book.

Challenges Encouraging Women into Manufacturing and STEM Fields

Some challenges exist to encourage women to consider a career in manufacturing and the STEM fields. One of the biggest deterrents is the perception that these fields are only for men. This perception has been changing since the 1970s when the women's revolution for equality in the workplace began to rise and take hold. I know this to be true because I have seen this take place firsthand in my career.

Other reasons are because the perception of what having a job in manufacturing is like continues to be outdated, such as: the jobs are low-skilled, low-paying, with no future potential for career growth, and the work environment is dirty. From my personal experience, both working in manufacturing for many years and my visiting over one hundred different manufacturing plants throughout my career, I can tell you that this negative stereotype is not true. Dirty plants and jobs are not the norm. Many plants are clean and bright with polished tile floors and painted walls. And they use innovative, high-tech machinery and processes to produce whatever they are making. The employees are highly trained and use their technical knowledge, skill, and experience to create quality products. Yes, there are dirty plants and jobs you and I would never want! But undesirable employment is present in *any* industry.

Another challenge to having more women choose STEM fields is many young girls and women believe they are "not good at math" because of societal messages they heard while growing up, which causes female students to have diminished confidence in their abilities to succeed in STEM subjects and careers.

In a study conducted by the Manufacturing Institute and the Deloitte company, the researchers found that "Women earn more than half of all associate, bachelor's, and master's degrees."[4] Are women capable? You bet! Women can excel in technical and scientific fields, which are a path to economic empowerment.

So what can we do to encourage more young women to enter into manufacturing and STEM fields? A starting point is to tell women a different story about what manufacturing and STEM are all about. Change societal messages to say that women *do* have the ability to succeed in math and other technical subjects and provide them access to relatable role models: women in manufacturing and STEM fields who they can look up to, and see themselves as, in the future.[5]

Men outnumber women in most manufacturing and STEM fields, but that doesn't mean it's hard for women to get jobs in these fields. Many forward-thinking companies have been hiring women for years now. They're ahead of their rivals because they've experienced the value women bring to their organizations, such as their collaborative approaches to problem-solving and relationship and listening skills: traits that foster teamwork and innovation.[6]

Employers also recognize that even though the demand for manufacturing and STEM-related jobs is growing, the pool of workers isn't.[7] This shortage of workers creates opportunities for women to find lucrative careers in these fields. The women interviewed in this book are proof that more women are entering and being welcomed into manufacturing and STEM fields and are succeeding.

The High Cost of College and Student Debt

The cost of a college education continues to rise. Farran Powell, a reporter at *U.S. News and World Report*, found that "the average cost of tuition and fees for the 2018–2019 school year was $35,676 at private colleges, $9,716 for state residents at public colleges, and $21,629 for out-of-state students at state schools, according to data reported to *U.S. News and World Report* in an annual survey."[8]

The company Student Loan Hero took a look at the 2018 student loan statistics: "Americans are more burdened by student loan debt than ever. In fact, the average student loan debt for Class of 2017 graduates was $39,400, up six percent from the previous year."[9] As worries and anxiety about student loan debt rise, anxious students and families are trying to figure out how to pay for four, or more, years of college.

Some jobs in manufacturing require a bachelor or an associate degree. Other jobs require a person to have vocational-technical training or a high school diploma, and on-the-job training. The time is right to make a case for, and explore, a much less expensive—and sometimes free to the student or worker—vocational-technical career. Low unemployment and a strong job market are exacerbating a growing skills gap, which is raising the employment prospects for skilled workers, putting them in an environment of high demand, and increasing wage rates.

Still, the decision to forego a four-year degree runs counter to thirty years of conventional wisdom. Today's students' parents come from a generation where most everyone got prepped to go to college. Many people considered vocational-technical careers as being for students who had less potential for success in college or who were "problem" students.[10]

Times have changed. The trades and vocational-technical careers are where the best opportunities exist today for the most significant number of people to earn above-average to high wages while incurring little to no student loan debt.

A little-known statistic is that forty-one percent of undergraduate students never get a college degree![11] A lower than expected college graduation rate has led to a course correction that is rippling through U.S. high schools; they are beginning to reemphasize a vocational-technical education.[12] So, it's an excellent time for students and parents to reexamine the educational and career paths out there.

High-school graduates looking for vocational-technical career training can not only find many programs at community colleges but also through a growing number of available apprenticeships at companies—some of which will pay for skills-based training and other required schooling, eliminating the need for incurring large amounts of student loan debt.

There are opportunities today to create an incredible career and a successful life, even if a person chooses not to go to college. Look around, and you will discover many people who have done just that. A colleague of mine, Bobi Siembieda, authored the book, *Ready! Set! Soar! Your Guide to Building a Career Without a College Degree* (pwnbooks.com/siembieda.htm). It includes tools and resources on how to build a successful career for those who decide that going to college isn't the best choice for them.

Going for a vocational education may be a hard sell in affluent areas for high-achieving students and their parents. But with more people finding out that going to college doesn't guarantee a decent, high-paying job, the field of manufacturing deserves a look. The splendid career success stories of the women in this book underscore this point.

A career in manufacturing isn't for everyone. A person must like several things: an industrial environment, machinery, and making things with equipment and tools; applying modern industrial science, engineering, technology, and math; and working with men, and being adaptable to, and comfortable in, an environment of constant change. For women who like these things, have a fascination for making things, and relish the complexity and challenge of making something like a precision part that goes into an aircraft engine, manufacturing is an excellent career choice!

Women can have vibrant, successful, and fulfilling careers in manufacturing, whether they choose to go to college, or not. The doors are open, and progressive business owners and other women who make are welcoming women into the industry with wide, open arms.

Manufacturing's Impact on the U.S. Economy

Manufacturing is making a strong comeback in the U.S. economy. "For decades people feared that cheap Chinese manufacturing would beat out the jobs of American workers. This was true for some time and many American companies outsourced to China for their manufacturing needs. As of recent, however, wages in China have jumped meaning that manufacturing has skyrocketed in price. Chinese goods used to easily outpace U.S.-made goods on price, but it is now only 5 percent cheaper to manufacture a product in China compared to here in the U.S. When you factor in all of the possible delays that come with international shipping and tariffs, many companies are now choosing to make their products here in America."[13]

Here are a few facts about manufacturing according to the National Association of Manufacturers:

> *"In 2017, manufacturing accounted for 11.6 percent of GDP in the economy. (Source: Bureau of Economic Analysis)"*[14]
>
> *"Every dollar spent in manufacturing adds another $1.89 to the economy."*[15]
>
> *"In 2017, the average manufacturing worker in the United States earned $84,832 annually, including pay and benefits. The average worker in all nonfarm industries earned $66,847. Looking specifically at wages, the average manufacturing worker earned more than $27 per hour, according to the latest figures, not including benefits. (Source:*

> *Bureau of Economic Analysis and Bureau of Labor Statistics)"*[16]
>
> *"Manufacturers have one of the highest percentages of workers who are eligible for health benefits provided by their employer. Indeed, 92 percent of manufacturing employees were eligible for health insurance benefits in 2015, according to the Kaiser Family Foundation. This is significantly higher than the 79 percent average for all firms."*[17]
>
> *"Over the next decade, nearly 3½ million manufacturing jobs will likely be needed, and 2 million are expected to go unfilled due to the skills gap. Moreover, according to a recent report, 80 percent of manufacturers report a moderate or serious shortage of qualified applicants for skilled and highly skilled production positions. (Source: Deloitte and the Manufacturing Institute)"*[18]

For these reasons, now is a good time to explore a career in manufacturing!

Manufacturing and STEM-Related Jobs

There are many exciting job opportunities in the manufacturing industry to explore if you like to:

- design and plan how to make things
- supervise people and make operations run smoothly
- solve problems and fix things
- find the solution to math problems
- set up and operate machines or robots to execute tasks or make products
- ensure that the products made in the plant are high quality
- program computerized and automated equipment
- support operations doing activities like shipping, receiving, and material handling
- work in an office and do administrative work
- be the CEO or president of your own company

As with any industry, some jobs are growing at a faster pace than others and offer more opportunities for people looking for work in those fields. The following chart lists some of the most common occupations in the manufacturing industry. Each job title is followed by the education level required for that job, and its annual median of earnings.

As you scan this list, keep in mind that there are many more types of manufacturing jobs than are included here, and jobs that require a college degree are higher paying than jobs that do not. For your own research, know that with a little probing, all the data listed can be found on the United States Department of Labor's Bureau of Labor Statistics website: bls.gov/home.htm.

Go to the next page to view the chart.

Job Title	What You Will Do	How to Become	Annual Earnings
Production Supervisor	Coordinate, plan, and direct workers and activities to create products. Oversee daily operations in manufacturing plants.	Promoted from within a company, typically after many years of work experience or by having a bachelor's degree and several years of work experience.	$100,580
Mechanical Engineer	Design, develop, build, and test manufacturing processes, tools, and equipment.	Bachelor's degree required.	$85,880
Industrial Engineer	Find ways to eliminate waste in production processes. Devise efficient systems that integrate workers, machines, materials, and information to make a product.	Bachelor's degree required.	$85,880
Occupational and Safety Specialist and Technician	Collect safety and accident data, and analyze work environments and procedures. Inspect workplaces to ensure adherence to safety, health, and environmental regulations to prevent harm to workers, property, and the public; you work to keep everyone safe.	Specialists typically need a bachelor's degree in occupational health and safety or in a related scientific or technical field. Technicians typically enter the occupation one of two ways: through on-the-job training, or through a postsecondary education, such as an associate degree or certificate.	$67,720
Electromechanical Technicians	Operate, test, and maintain unmanned, automated, robotic, or electromechanical equipment.	Typically need either an associate degree or a post-secondary certificate.	$56,740
CNC (Computer Numerical Control) Machine Tool Programmers	Develop programs to control the machining or processing of metal or plastic parts executed by automatic machine tools, equipment, or systems.	Most CNC machine tool programmers are skilled machinists and have several years of experience. They receive on-the-job training. Some have an associate degree in mechanical engineering or other technical degree.	$55,770
Maintenance Technician	Maintain and repair equipment and other industrial machinery to ensure they are working properly.	Typically need a high school diploma and at least one year of on-the-job training.	$50,440
CNC Machinists and Tool and Die Makers	Set up and operate a variety of CNC (Computer Numerical Control) and mechanically controlled machine tools to produce precision metal parts, instruments, and tools.	Typically need to complete training and courses beyond high school and receive on-the-job training, go through apprentice-ship programs, and attend vocational schools or community and technical colleges. Many employers pay for the full cost of training because of the shortage of these workers.	$44,110
Welders, Solderers, Cutters and Brazers	Use handheld or remotely controlled equipment to join or cut metal parts, or fill holes, indentations, or seams.	A high school diploma or equivalent, combined with technical and on-the-job training.	$40,240
Quality Control Inspector	Examine products and materials for defects or deviations from specifications. They make sure products made are high quality.	Most quality control inspectors need a high school diploma and receive on-the-job training. Training time can vary between one month to one year.	$37,340
Machine Operator	Set up and operate machines that cut, shape, and form metal and plastic materials or pieces.	Most metal and plastic workers have a high school diploma and learn through on-the-job training, typically lasting one year.	$35,400
Assembler and Fabricator	Assemble finished products, which can include assembling the parts that go into final products. Use tools, machines, and hands to assemble/make products. Also test final products to ensure they work properly.	Education level and qualifications vary per industry and employer. A high school diploma is adequate for most jobs. Experience and additional training are needed for more advanced assembly work.	$31,850

PART 2: STORIES AND INTERVIEWS

Bonita Richter, MBA

Title: Finance Executive, and I was groomed to be father's successor

Company: Troutman Industries, Inc.

Location: West Lawn, Pennsylvania

Manufacturing Processes: CNC Precision Machining of plastic and metal components (plastics machining was our specialty), Precision Hard-Chrome Plating, and Plastic Stamping*

Industries Served: Aerospace, Chemical, Paper and Pulp, Machinery and Equipment, Electronic, Instrumentation, Defense, Medical, and others

Examples of Products Made: Machined components that went into the instrument panels of aircraft engines and computer control boards; commercial-use chemical pumps that would direct the flow of fluids; valves for paper-making machinery that would control the flow of needed chemicals; telecommunications equipment and fiber optics; instrument panels for U.S. Navy ships and submarines; dental and medical diagnostic equipment; stamped plastic washers suitable for a variety of industrial uses

Number of Employees: 49

Personal Interests: Family, watercolor painting, gardening, home decorating, needlepoint, baking bread, entertaining, reading nonfiction, horses, and cats

• • •

My Father, My Mentor

Today has Changed from Yesterday

As women, we have come so far, and have made significant strides towards social, economic, educational, and professional equality, though there is still some progress to be made.

My story is about some of the experiences and challenges I faced, and what things were like for me when I started my career in manufacturing back in the 1970s when there weren't many women working in the industry. You'll learn about the opportunities that helped spur my career growth, as well as the setbacks I experienced while navigating my way as a young woman coming of age in the '70s and '80s. Through my story, I hope you will see how different things are today for women—not only for women in manufacturing but also for all career women.

Even from the time when I began working in manufacturing, though, I saw women being increasingly welcomed into the industry—they were not only working on the shop floor, but also serving in management and leadership positions. Today, women are earning more bachelor's degrees than men are.[19] The gender pay gap, though it still exists, is closing. Women are marrying at a later age since the rise of the feminist movement that began in the early 1960s,[20] which was influenced by the Civil Rights Movement,[21] and they are choosing to have children at a later age, too. In 1962, most women married for the first time when they were just over twenty years old, whereas in 2018, most women married for the first time when they were almost twenty-nine years old.[22] In 1970, most women gave birth to their first child when they were about twenty-one and a half years old, but in 2016, the average age was twenty-six.[23]

I didn't accomplish what I did in my career alone. I had a lot of help, guidance, and support from two incredible mentors, my father and a business coach, as well as many other people in the manufacturing industry along the way. Though neither my family nor I still own or operate our manufacturing business, Troutman Industries, Inc., I am still involved in manufacturing as an executive adviser to CEOs and presidents of organizations and companies on strategy, leadership development, and transforming culture, and I deliver my services through my own consulting firm, Profit Strategies.

Here is my story. I hope you enjoy reading it.

Setting the Stage

I was born on December 13, 1962, in Reading, Pennsylvania, two months after the Cuban Missile Crisis and eleven months before President John F. Kennedy's death. As 1963 began, Americans were optimistic about the economy and thought it possible that the U.S. could achieve a peaceful relationship with Russia. Civil rights became the overwhelming issue of 1963, and on a wind-swept February 7, 1964, the British rock-and-roll band, the Beatles, arrived at John F. Kennedy International Airport, in New York City, for their first U.S. visit, sparking "Beatlemania."

My mother, RuthAnn, was a housewife and stay-at-home mom. In 1960, society expected a woman to follow one path: to marry in her early 20s, quickly start a family, and devote her life to homemaking. My mother's life followed this path. She had wanted to become a schoolteacher, but her family didn't have the money to send her to college. So, she took her other option: she got married, as most women did from her generation. She and my father married on September 10, 1960, just a few months after she graduated from high school. By February 6, 1971, she had four children under the age of eight.

I had an ordinary childhood, except for having a father who was an entrepreneur that owned his own business. The entrepreneurial spirit of passion, positivity, leadership, and ambition infiltrated every part of our home life, and is in my blood.

One of my earliest memories is when I was three years old, holding my mother's hand, looking around the shop floor of my father's manufacturing company on Butler Street in Reading, Pennsylvania, that he owned. I remember the unpainted concrete floor and the grey machines standing at attention around the perimeter of the walls. Oil and other industrial smells filled my nostrils, a poignant scent that always brings back a flood of positive childhood memories and feelings of comfort. Even at that early age, I sensed that my father, Gerald E. "Jerry" Troutman, was in charge.

How Our Family's Business Began

After my father graduated in 1952 from Reading High School, in Reading, Pennsylvania, he began attending the Wyomissing Polytechnic Institute[24] in Wyomissing, Pennsylvania, to study the fields of mechanical engineering, engineering technology, and to receive training to become a machinist.

He attended classes by day. By night, he worked as an apprentice machinist at the Polymer Corporation[25] in Reading (as of this writing, this company is now Quadrant EPP USA, Inc.), which made extruded (i.e., shaped), engineered (i.e., chemically mixed) plastics and machined components.

Engineered plastics are used in high-tech, innovative applications and products where the parts made often need to be strong, and highly resistant to impact, abrasion, and/or heat. Components made of engineered plastics are used in military, chemical, food service, and many other applications where these physical performance qualities are required. Some examples of the different types of engineered advanced plastics are ABS (Acrylonitrile Butadiene Styrene), Nylon 6 and 6-6, Polycarbonate, Acetal, and Teflon.

After my dad worked at Polymer for a few years, his supervisor, Carroll Harrison, left the company to start his own business. My father decided to follow Carroll and worked for him as a machinist, machining precision plastic and metal parts on manual lathes, mills, and drill presses.

I asked my uncle David why my father left Polymer and was willing to take the risk of leaving a good, steady job to work in Carroll's small, startup, two-man machine shop. This is what he told me:

> *"Carroll Harrison was a brilliant mechanical engineer and machinist. Your dad knew he wanted to start his own business, and he knew that if he stayed at Polymer he'd be doing what he was doing, machining in the shop, for a long time. So, when Carroll left, he left too. He saw this as an opportunity to learn from Carroll by being able to work closely with him to learn the engineering and machinist trade, and to find a better way to achieve his goal of starting his own business.*

> *He quickly got that opportunity. Six weeks later, after Carroll moved into his new shop, there was a fire that killed him. That same day of the fire, your dad went to the purchasing agents at Western Electric and Bell Labs on 11th Street. They knew Carroll had died in the fire. Your dad told them he could do the work, that he had his own equipment. They gave the work to your dad, and he was in business."*

This event, though tragic, was what launched my father into starting his own manufacturing business, Troutman Machine Shop, in the basement of his parents' home in Reading, on, as my father always used to note when telling his story, Lincoln's birthday (February 12) in 1960.

A few months later, the purchasing agents at Western Electric and Bell Labs, being very pleased with his work, awarded my father a large contract for precision-machined parts. This contract enabled him to move his business out of the basement of his parents' home and into the small rented space on Butler Street where I knew my dad's business to be. Soon, my father realized that he needed help to get all of the work done, so my uncle, David Troutman, became my father's first employee, joining the business shortly after he turned nineteen years old. A few years later, my dad's father, Lester Troutman, joined the company too. My father created a family business from the start.

First Immersions

When I was seven years old, my father would take my sisters and me with him to "the shop." When we were there, I remember him doing one of two things: making parts on a milling machine that spewed tiny, shiny metal chips on the floor, or sitting behind his desk writing something that we knew was important. As he worked on the machine, I remember him telling us, "Don't bump into the handles of the machines," as we took turns galloping around the aisles, pulling a hand truck with red-painted wooden handles behind us while we played "horse."

When he worked in the office, we "worked" with him. We made copies of everything—of the stapler, paper clips, pens, and even our hands and faces—using the new Xerox® copy machine. We also played with the intercom system, broadcasting announcements, and typed up pretend invoices.

When I was between the ages of eight and thirteen years old, my father was always there but he was in the background of my life. Back-to-back recessions in 1970, and then political and financial issues in the years 1973–1975 made for a difficult business environment.[26] "The Organization of the Petroleum Exporting Countries is blamed for quadrupling oil prices."[27] Inflation, stagflation, and unemployment peaking at 9 percent in May of 1975, made life difficult all around for many middle-class Americans.[28] It was a lean time. Dinner was often pancakes and waffles smothered in lots of butter and sugar, macaroni pasta made with powdered cheese out of a box, or tuna or ground beef Hamburger Helper. But as kids, we weren't aware of that and didn't mind having this tasty, convenient, and budget-friendly food for dinner. During those years, my father worked long hours, leaving in the morning before I woke up, and not getting home until 10:00 p.m., or even later in the early morning hours of the following day if he had to deliver parts to customers. Consequently, my mother was my world. My father was this figure that appeared at certain times. Yet when he was around, his soft gray-blue eyes lit up along with a playful grin that showed he was genuinely glad to see me.

My father's influence on my life became more prominent when I started working with him at the machine shop as a teenager. He was the bridge between my being a youngster at home with my mother and my stepping into young adulthood.

I started my first "real" job at the shop when I was thirteen years old. Early on Saturday mornings, my father would wake my younger sister and me up to go with him to the plant. We'd blast the music that played on the local rock-and-roll radio station as we cleaned, de-burred, and polished plastic parts that were used in chemical pumping equipment until they gleamed. We worked until lunchtime, and then a weekend of play began.

When I was fifteen years old, I started working at the shop on second shift over the summers, and during the school year, I worked on weekends. This is when my first apprenticeship began. The first machine I operated was a Hardinge DMSA automatic turret lathe, which was an automated machine where the tools were programmed to automatically move into position to machine the parts, rather than having to move the tools into place by hand. I made stainless steel components that were used in the mold-making industry.

I want to give you a real idea of what working on a machine like this was like, so that you'll have a sense of what it was like then as well as now. All of the machining operations on a Hardinge DMSA took place inside a clear, hard-plastic canopy that covered its spinning parts, which was a good thing because the canopy kept the oil used in the machining processes inside of the machine (instead of all over me), and it protected me from the fast-spinning, moving mechanical parts.

After the machine finished making the part, a tool moved over to the now machined piece to cut it off from the bar of metal material sticking out of the collet. A collet has a hole in the center that exerts a strong clamping force and tightens around the raw material, or a machined shape, to hold it in place so that it does not deflect away from the pressure the machine's tools exert on it to shape it or cut it. Simultaneously, a metal slide (shaped much like a sliding board) powered by pneumatic (air) pressure moved up to the part to catch it as it was cut off. Then the part slid down the slide into a metal pan that collected the machined parts, which lay in a shallow pool of oil.

Then I had to machine and shape a flange—a rim that flared out at the top of the part the DSMA machine made (imagine a funnel but with a flatter, shorter slope at the top)—by using a second-operation lathe, a much smaller machine than the DSMA automatic turret lathe. I had to operate the tools on this machine manually: I would put the pieces into the collet of this lathe one at a time. The collet clamped tightly around the part. Then I would pull a handle to start the motor of the machine and it would spin the part around. I would manually move the cutting tool in place to machine the part by taking hold of the long handle of the machine and moving my right hand and wrist toward the left in a smooth motion. Once the flange was machined, I pulled the handle and tool back to the right to its starting position. It was easy to get into a rhythm operating the two machines, which made my work shift pass quickly.

Another one of my job specialties was tapping metal threads into tiny brass parts, .188 inch in diameter, using a drill press with an attached spring collet. As the name suggests, a spring collet has a hole with a small spring inside of it. I had to press each brass part against the spring and then close the collet to hold the part in place. The spring collet's purpose was to "pop" the piece out of the collet after the threads were tapped into the brass part. The production manager always gave me this job because the men, with their larger fingers, had a much harder time handling these small parts: they'd often fumble, and the spring collet would launch the tiny pieces into the air, and they'd be lost forever!

I loved working in the shop. The night shifts went by quickly because I was busy working three machines, the music of the '70s was playing on the loudspeakers, and the men in the shop were always willing to answer my questions or sharpen a tool for me.

Where I Belong

It is curious that the place where I belonged in the world—working beside my father in a mechanical, industrial place—would present itself so early in my life. By sheer random chance, I was born in a time and place to a particular father. I didn't realize it then, but something had called me to experience and embrace what was extraordinary for a young woman at that time: to be raised in a manufacturing environment, and nurtured to succeed, and lead my father's company one day.

I was five years old when the feminist movement of the late 1960s rose. Of course, I didn't know this was happening, but, being a child of the times, I was absorbing this positive change in our American culture and was straddling the two worlds of traditional norms expected of women (as my mother had experienced), and their liberation from them. The women's liberation movement of the late 1960s and 1970s focused on dismantling workplace inequality and fought to give women more access to higher education and workplace opportunities, pushing women over the barricades that separated them from power and privilege.

You could see our culture shifting through the media. I grew up watching *Bewitched, The Brady Bunch,* and *I Dream of Jeannie* on TV, which depicted stay-at-home moms and women playing out much more conservative family roles.

Then with the '70s came *The Mary Tyler Moore Show,* revolutionary for its time, which was about a single, financially independent young woman living on her own in the city. *The Partridge Family* was a show about a musical, widowed mother whose children convinced her to join them in their garage band recording sessions. They recorded a hit record and then traveled around the country to perform in a primary-colored, geometric-patterned refurbished school bus. And then there was *Charlie's Angels,* which was a crime drama about smart women who were trained as private detectives, successful in the world of espionage, and knew and used martial arts.

In 1976, when I entered ninth grade, for the first time in our country's cultural history, women were being told that they were just as capable as men and could be whatever they wanted to be. Throughout high school and college, I devoutly believed I could be a successful career woman no matter what I chose to do. I never doubted that I wouldn't be able to do it all—or have it all. But I know now that my father instilled some of that confidence in me, too, as I worked with him in the shop.

Looking back at that time, what is interesting is my mother didn't give me any guidance at all about going to college, having a career, or even what my choices were to make about my life. It probably didn't enter her mind because her perception was that my life would be like hers. It was my high school guidance counselors who drilled into me the importance of going to college, and I didn't question what they were telling me because all my classmates were getting the same message: go to college.

College: A False Start

On a humid summer day in August 1980, I drove to Pennsylvania State University's Berks Campus to attend the first day of classes of my freshman year. My major was pre-med; I wanted to be an equine veterinarian. My first-term course load consisted of chemistry, zoology, algebra, and freshman English. Though I had the intellect to study these subjects, I found I had a lack of interest, and perhaps maturity, to do my studies well.

That lack of interest became serious. I'd stopped attending classes a few weeks into the spring term. But my parents brought me up to not be a quitter, so at once, I looked for a job. I was offered and took the first job I applied for: working as a full-time salesperson at Bakers Shoes in the mall.

I loathed everything about that job! I not only had to work during summer days but nights and weekends, too. Less than two months into the job, I quit.

Not feeling too good about myself, and needing to be doing something with my time and life, I mustered up the courage to ask my father if he had a job for me at the machine shop. It so happened my timing was perfect. President Reagan's promise of economic prosperity had buoyed the growth of my father's business. He needed help processing the increased number of purchase orders from customers and with ordering and buying the raw materials needed to make the plastic and metal components his company manufactured.

He told me he would hire me on one condition: that I would go back to school and get an education. A few weeks later, in August of 1981, I was taking my first business class: small business management. It was with taking this class that I discovered that I loved business!

College, Career, Hearth, and Home

One year later, on September 11, 1982, I got married at nineteen years of age. On December 7, 1985, I welcomed my first child, a son. I continued attending night school at Penn State while working full time. In 1986, I earned my first degree: an associate degree in science, business administration. My life was on a three-tiered path of college, career, and tradition. By the time I was twenty-nine years old I had three children, a son and two daughters, and was attending night school, taking two courses a term, working to earn a bachelor's degree.

Although I was born at the cusp of the feminist movement, traditional family values strongly influenced my life, and I wasn't an anomaly. All of my friends got married in their early 20s and had children shortly after that, too. Some started college and got degrees, but many didn't. It was a time of transition for women. We were still trying to figure out how to become what the women's liberation movement said we could become and how to make that happen.

My father supported me tremendously as I worked hard at both work and my personal life and guided me toward a successful career—one many women were working toward for the first time in those years, but to explain how he did that, you need to know a little more about him.

Troutman Family Values

My father's values and personality were shaped by time and place. He was born in Reading, Pennsylvania on January 26, 1935, in the middle of the Great Depression. Like so many, his family did not have a lot of money. His father, Lester Herman Troutman, was a blue-collar worker, working in a factory as a knitter making women's stockings. His mother, Helen Gertrude (Beckey) Troutman, worked at a company that made whimsical signs, and minded the home. She ran a tight ship: everything was in order and had its place.

An interesting note is that both of my father's parents always had jobs and earned an income during the Great Depression, which kept them out of the dire financial straits that affected so many other families at that time. This is fortunate, and also provides clues about the strong character, and industrious nature of my father's parents.

My grandmother imparted her Pennsylvania German work ethic to her son, and she also taught him the ideals of gentlemanliness—speaking with reserve, holding himself correctly, and behaving courteously and kindly. His mother insisted he wear a suit and tie when he went on dates with young women on Friday and Saturday nights.

He judiciously completed his schoolwork, studied hard to get As, and squeezed in time for private dancing lessons. He was not an aggressive man and took a calm, measured approach to all things.

Through this disciplined upbringing, my father became a self-made, self-reliant man. He would often tell stories about how he burned the midnight oil when he was studying to become a mechanical engineer at Wyomissing Polytechnic Institute. Working hard, applying oneself to do one's best, and maintaining order were strong family values passed on from generation to generation.

My Father's Mentor

In the early days of my father's business, Joseph "Joe" Boscov, a well-established, successful businessman in the Reading area, became my father's mentor. Joe's parents and brother owned several successful retail establishments in the area and had a long history of entrepreneurial success that began in 1911.[29]

Joe, himself, owned a company that made plastic-coated wire, and he would stop in at my father's business to have my dad do some work for him. Joe, knowing my father was new in business, would always ask him how things were going. The two would talk, and my father would run ideas that he had by Joe. Joe supported my dad's plans and gave him guidance and advice during the early days of my father being in business. I don't think it would ever have occurred to them that they had a mentor/mentee relationship because that arrangement wasn't common in those days like it is today.

Even after my father had been in business for over forty years, he often spoke about Joe and the things he had learned from him. Without a doubt, Joe was very influential in my father's life. Dad would tell many stories about what he learned from Joe. The words of advice he would most often repeat were the ones Joe said to him one day: "Jerry, save your pennies because one day those pennies will become dollars." My father heeded this advice, always being fastidious about managing how he spent and invested his money.

I don't know if this experience of having a mentor made my father want to mentor others, but I know he did because of the stories I heard from people who worked for him. Person after person told me the same thing: that they wouldn't be where they are today in their careers if it were not for my father "taking them under his wing" in the machine shop, and patiently guiding and teaching them the skills they needed to become better machinists.

The Early Years: Growing the Business

As I said, my father's first customer was Bell Telephone Laboratories ("Bell Labs"), a communications, scientific, and engineering company, and E.I. DuPont de Nemours Engineering Laboratories, a chemical company that developed plastics, was his second customer.

Business relationships had a more casual approach back then. My uncle David told me that after he and my father machined the requested parts for DuPont, he would drive down to the plant in Delaware to deliver them. He'd always stop in at the purchasing department and talk to the two buyers there to ask them if they had any more work. Often, he'd be shown a blueprint, look at it, and then tell the buyers, "Yes, we can do this." He'd take the print back to the shop, and he and my father would start the work that evening.

That's how getting work happened in those days: you went out knocking on doors looking for work, found it, sealed the deal with a handshake, and made the parts. In today's world, getting work is a much more formalized process, with requests for proposals being sent out to a multitude of companies for bids, that first have to pass through and be approved by multiple levels of purchasing personnel, to eventually having the purchase order contracts sludge their way through the corporate bureaucratic system.

My father was a forward-thinking man as well as an entrepreneur. Always one of the first to adopt new technology, my father bought the company's first Numerical Control (NC) machines in 1971. These were programmable, automated pieces of equipment in which the movement of the different parts of the machinery was controlled by punched paper tape. These machines were used for the "production runs" of larger quantities of parts that had to be repeatedly made with precise measurements. These machines could consistently maintain measurements to the thousandths of an inch (this precise crafting is crucial for parts that are placed in airplane engines and the like), so that when assembling a product, the individual pieces that were assembled into a part would all fit well together.

My uncle David told me these machines were "slow readers." They would take a command, but you had to wait (and watch the motionless tools) a full five seconds before they moved to begin cutting the material.

When my dad bought those first NC machines in 1971, he told David, "Learn how to run these." David learned, and he discovered he loved programming. So he was excited when in 1976, my father purchased two of the first-generation CNC (Computer Numerical Control) machines. Digital technology had entered the fray. Automation in production processes increased the rate of production, and manufacturing metal and plastic machined parts became more efficient and faster than ever. David became the technology wizard at the company, and the chief NC / CNC programming engineer and problem solver.

My Father

My father was a well-respected and brilliant man. His reserved nature and self-control masked a man of deep emotion and passion. Though he was of average build, he had a commanding presence when he walked into a room and brought an air of warmth, humbleness, and confidence with him. Unlike many leaders, my father was not an egoist. His qualities of general kindness, and the basic decency and fairness with which he treated everyone made him an indispensable leader.

He was proud to be a leader and the president of his own company for forty-two years, Troutman Industries, Inc., which was indeed a family business. There was a time when family members made up nearly 20 percent of its employees.

My sisters, Theresa ("Terrie") and Patricia ("Patty"), also worked in the family business from the time they were twelve years old. They cleaned, de-burred, and polished plastic parts, just like I did. Later, as an adult, Terrie worked from home polishing and finishing parts. Patty earned an industrial engineering degree and got involved in time studies, improving productivity and programming, and making changes to our network software; she has the "Troutman engineering brain," just like my father and uncle David. My brother, Eric, worked in the shop as a CNC machinist and welder. Terrie's husband, Donald, worked at the company as a quality control inspector. And I worked in many areas of the company, too.

We were a high-functioning family business: there were no disputes or power struggles amongst the family members. The reason was because my father demonstrated unequivocally strong leadership and voiced explicit expectations about our behavior as "Troutmans" while at work. This behavior served as a model for the other employees to follow, such as immediately getting up from the lunch table when the end-of-break bell rang, getting to work on time, and never being absent, to name a few examples. Conducting oneself with decorum in the workplace was insisted upon, and personal matters stayed outside of the business, where they belonged. These behaviors were the key to the respect that our family members earned from the other employees, which was a crucial component of the company's long-term success.

We had an incredible group of employees. They called my father "The General" with the greatest respect and admiration. He knew how to take charge and handle every situation, knowing we would all succeed, no matter what the challenge. He was a forward thinker, a pioneer, and always one of the first to adopt and incorporate new technology. During my interview with my uncle David, he told me, "I had the greatest job in the world. I had the greatest boss in the world." I wholeheartedly agree with him.

Jerry Troutman was a legend in the East Coast precision-machining-job-shop scene. Everyone in the industry either knew him or knew of him. Locally, other community leaders sought his advice and participation in countless industry committees. He was a leader in the community in both industry and civic matters. At meetings, he didn't blather in a long-winded way like so many others who wanted to show how intelligent they were. He would listen, and when he formed his thoughts, he spoke. A quiet word from him echoed loudly: people listened to what Jerry Troutman had to say.

Locally, he proudly served as the president of the Reading Rotary International Club, the president of a local credit union, and he was the co-chairman of the Berks County Private Industry Council. In 1988, the Berks County Chamber of Commerce awarded my father the Small Business Person of the Year award.

One of my father's top values was education. He was always learning and was known to always have a business book in his hand, reading and taking notes from them every day. He was continuously teaching others what he was learning. Being way ahead of others in the manufacturing industry by foreseeing the critical nature of the impending skilled labor shortage that the manufacturing industry and skilled machinist trade is experiencing today, and being one to put his words and values into action, in the early 1990s he established the Machine Tool Technology associate degree program at the Reading Area Community College,[30] which is still being offered today. Deeply invested in educating others, he also served as an advisor to the Berks Career & Technology Center CNC machinist program.

My father was also politically active and often took part in hearings at Pennsylvania's state capitol and at Capitol Hill in Washington, D.C., to address legislative issues and advance the manufacturing industry. Growth and expansion in the community where he lived were vital to him. He was also a philanthropist and donated money to many capital campaign projects for local universities, colleges, vocational schools, museums, and other cultural and industry projects.

The manufacturing community, industry-wide magazine publications, and local newspaper journalists frequently interviewed him to find out what his secrets to success were. Part of his humble answer was always the same: "I made more good decisions than bad ones."

What a blessing it was to have such a wonderful father and mentor in my life. He brought me up and taught me everything he knew about business. Ever patient, he was never too busy to answer my constant questions or explain to me how to do something. He made me feel worthy of his time and attention.

He served as an excellent role model for leadership, took my hand and guided me through the growth of my career, and groomed me to succeed him and run the company one day. He modeled everything for me from how to work a machine, to how to gauge the measurements of a machined part, to how to work with people.

My father gave me the opportunity to shine and opened doors for me that most likely would have remained closed if it had not been for him and his influence. His mentorship gave me an opportunity to be seen, and have my voice heard, because I was Jerry Troutman's daughter. The respect people had for my father paved the way for me.

Loving Business

My father supported my ascension in the company by giving me opportunities to work in many different areas of the company over the twenty-seven years I worked by his side. I had jobs in shipping and prepared and packaged parts for shipment to customers and suppliers for metal finishing. In receiving, when shipments from suppliers were delivered, I checked to make sure that what we received were the correct goods ordered, that they were in good condition, and in the correct quantities ordered.

On the shop floor, I worked as a machine operator on automatic CNC and manual equipment. In customer service, I answered phone calls and expedited customers' orders. Then I was promoted to order entry and purchasing to prepare customer orders for production, ordered materials, set up a computerized inventory management system, managed inventory levels, assembled required blueprints and other information for production, and entered the order information into the MRPII (Manufacturing Resource Planning II) system, which is a production planning computer system that assists in scheduling work on the required machinery and equipment to make the parts. The MRPII system integrated with other business information, such as customer, personnel, inventory, accounting, and finance information.

Later on, I took on human resources duties, where I hired personnel, implemented performance management reviews, delivered training, implemented an employee assistance program, and dealt with a variety of personnel issues.

In production I helped form team projects to address high volume or frequently requested orders. As a team, we worked to achieve the best production and efficiency rates possible, and in doing so, reduced the cost of production. We used a program called Just-In-Time (JIT) manufacturing, which incorporated set-up time reduction and Kanban, an inventory management system. In general, JIT helped us get perfect amounts of product onto the shop floor, exactly where and when it needed to be, consistently and smoothly. I also facilitated implementing a new tooling management and Kanban inventory system, which made sure we had the tools we used most often delivered to us right when we needed them, which decreased our tooling costs. I also established a safety program and a safety committee.

For quality control, I helped write ISO 9001 standard quality compliance policies and procedures documentation along with my uncle David and the quality control manager at the time. I helped with inside sales, primarily as an order taker, and with outside sales, where I accompanied my father to trade shows and meetings with our largest clients in the Northeast.

I created and wrote the quarterly company newsletter for marketing purposes, and was eventually promoted to finance manager, which was the highest position I rose to in the company. I never had the opportunity to become president of the company, although I had been groomed for the job, because we decided to sell the business.

Except for my father and uncle David, no one else in the company had this experience or had done all that I had in so many different areas in the business. My job experience was unique and was preparing me to succeed my father and lead the company one day, and it was why I ascended in the company and was able to earn the respect of the employees. I wasn't handed a high-ranking job just because I was the boss's daughter. Working in the business side of the business, and working for my father, was such a great fit for me, I blossomed.

My Other Mentor: The Business Doctor

At the time I was in charge of customer order entry and purchasing, another influential mentor emerged in my life. My father hired a business coach to teach me how to develop a strategic plan. His name was W. Kent Kise, Jr.

Kent was president of his own manufacturing company, and just like my father, was an active, award-winning community business leader. "Having authored the business book entitled *Prescription for Winning the Game of Business*, based on his regular column in the Business Month section in the *Lancaster New Era* [newspaper], Kent was often referred to as the 'Business Doctor' by many of Lancaster's business owners, managers, and not-for-profit executive directors. He was known for his 'to the point,' concise and practical advice which was always enriched with his sense of humor."[31]

Kent was a wise, warm-hearted, white-haired gentleman with eyes that sparkled when he laughed. It wasn't uncommon for him to break out into song while we worked together: he used to sing in chorus lines in musical theater productions.

I remember that during the recession of 1991–92 he guided me about what I could do to help improve sales and profits when other companies like ours were going out of business. The actions he recommended to take were simple, and they worked. Kent advocated for me to move into the finance manager position because he saw my enthusiasm for the discipline of finance and recognized that what I was learning at Penn State would provide immediate value to the company. I was learning how to do things such as how to do capital asset planning, how to calculate the payback period on an investment, and calculate the net present value of future cash flow—all valuable tools when making capital investment decisions in business.

This move resulted in a significant and positive career shift for another person at the company. A highly skilled and seasoned machinist working in the plant was given the opportunity to take over my job of order entry and purchasing. Because of this change, he was able to invest some of his time teaching other employees to improve their machinist skills. He also became one of the instructors at the Machine Tool Technology program at the Reading Area Community College that my father founded. This story is an example that there are opportunities for career growth in manufacturing no matter where you start your career path. This is as true today as it was back then.

Kent, like my father, was someone who truly cared about my success. What was remarkable about this was the respect he had for women working in the manufacturing industry, who, at the time, were not seen as having high potential for leading businesses, much less ones in manufacturing. He also saw me in the role of being my father's successor and coached me on developing my business skills and professional presence as a young woman in this male-dominated industry. He even accompanied me to a seminar in Lancaster, Pennsylvania, titled "Develop Your Professional Presence," and supportively coached me on how I could immediately and powerfully apply what I was learning.

One day while walking to our favorite place for lunch after a morning of productive work together, I distinctly remember Kent saying to me, "Don't try to act or be like a man." He thought this was a mistake that many women made, which thwarted their success in what they were trying to achieve. Instead, he encouraged me to use my feminine skills and charm, strive to present myself with poise and confidence, and to always dress professionally to garner respect and win others over. That advice worked too.

Lost Mentorship Opportunity

So, the two most influential mentors in my life were both males. I didn't have any female mentors. At the time, I knew of only one woman in manufacturing. She was the president of a local business; her father had wanted her to lead his company once he retired, and so passed the business to her. It didn't cross my mind to ask her to mentor me because I had already had two great teachers. I vaguely recall that she offered to meet with me to talk about being a woman in the industry.

I never took her up on that offer, though. Today, I understand how valuable that conversation could have been to me. Back then, I didn't realize that being a woman in manufacturing was an oddity because manufacturing had been a big part of my life from the time I was born. It is true that there were very few women in manufacturing at the time. It was a man's world. But I didn't recognize it in that way back then because of the high level of support I was receiving from the men around me in the industry.

Today, more women are involved and are shattering the glass ceilings in manufacturing. The idea that it used to be a place where women didn't choose to work may seem an absurd notion in our modern times. Any woman who worked in the manufacturing industry back in the '60s, '70, '80s, and even into the '90s, will tell you that things for women in the industry have massively changed since then.

One of those things is that mentorship possibilities have greatly expanded, and mentorships can come more readily from women now too, as will be seen in the interviews in this book. The opportunity to be mentored by other women is one of the most significant changes I have seen in the industry over the last three decades, and that more women are involved at leadership levels in manufacturing!

No matter what career you choose, or when you're deciding where you want to work, ask what type of mentorship opportunities are accessible to you, and what type of career paths are available. You want to look for a company that supports career development and growth for their employees, and has established, mentor-apprenticeship or other training programs in place. Having someone to encourage, teach, and advocate for you changes the trajectory of your career and life path.

Learning from Men

It was something special to be brought up by a father—and other men, too—in the manufacturing industry. I grew up in an environment where people solved problems every day.

Let me offer you an example. My family's company made parts using CNC precision machining. Here's how precise this technology is: CNC precision machining uses computers to operate sophisticated pieces of high-tech machinery (machine tools) and give commands to run multi-step processes to make components (metal and plastic parts) that meet specifications on customers' blueprints. The tolerances our company worked with (deviations from stated dimensions on a blueprint) were typically plus or minus .0002 inches. How small is .0002 inches? A human hair is .002 inch in diameter. If you take a piece of hair and split it into 100 pieces, each piece is .0002 inch in size.

So many things need to go right to be able to produce a precision part, and it's not uncommon to face challenges along the way. Examples of typical problems are attributed to what's known as the 5 M's of the lean manufacturing philosophy: Man, Material, Machines, Methods, and Money. Lean manufacturing, also known as lean production, is a systematic way to reduce waste in the manufacturing process in order to reduce cost and increase productivity and output.

What I saw from the men I worked with was that they tackled problems head-on. They didn't question if they could fix something or make it work. Instead, they figured out how they would do it. They didn't hesitate because of fear of things perhaps not working—they forged ahead and acted. They planned their approach and their plan of attack to solve a problem. Then they executed their plan, and if it didn't work out the first time, they merely changed the approach and worked until they got it right. They always ended up getting it right; I never heard any of them say something was "impossible" to do or that they "gave up."

From my father and the other men I worked with, I learned all about planning, strategizing, working together to solve problems, taking on challenges and not being fearful of the outcome, and working at something until you get it right.

I didn't realize it then, but working alongside my father was the greatest gift I could ever receive in my life. Working with him unquestionably made my life easier: I had a career path, worked closely with someone who cared about me, guided me, and wanted me to succeed.

But coming of age as a woman in manufacturing wasn't easy.

Having It All

To contrast how things are different today for women in manufacturing, indeed in any career, from when I started, I want to share more of my personal experience. My story is but one that shows how much societal attitudes and the workplace environment has changed and improved over the last fifty years for women.

Like so many women, American society raised me to believe I could have whatever I wanted, when I wanted it. I could have a career, and children, whenever I chose. I felt I could seamlessly move from being a wife, mother, and career girl up to the boardroom and beyond.

I vividly remember a commercial for Enjoli perfume.[32] It showed a sultry blonde woman strutting home after a successful day at the office, then slinking in a tight dress toward a supposed husband while she sang a proactive little song, which I can recall exactly: "I can bring home the bacon, fry it up in the pan. And never let you forget you're a man. 'Cause I'm a woman.' Enjoli."

This perfume commercial jingle was the anthem for young girls and women of the time and showed a go-getting working wife coming home after a long day at work to tend to hearth, home, children, and husband, set with a warm, spicy undertone. This impression of what a successful working wife looked like became emblazoned in my mind, and I presumed my life would be just like the woman's in the commercial for Enjoli.

In Between Worlds

In March 1986, I had just returned to work after the birth of my first child. Michael David was twelve weeks old. The only private room was the bathroom, so I perched on the lone "chair" in there, the toilet, in the 12' x 12' bathroom, while the breast pump machine I was using hummed loudly. There was no private "mother's lounge," as there are, fortunately, in many companies today.

The bathroom was right next to the break room with the soda and snack machine, and the shipping department, and there were always a few men in the area. I knew the men had to be able to hear the rhythmic humming of the machine. So, when I finished, I tried as casually as I could to walk out of the bathroom door, and it was then when I realized, ironically, that I was "having it all."

When my son was eight months old, I returned to Penn State for the fall term. Working during the day and going to school at night . . . it was hard juggling everything. Yet as hard as it was, I was entertaining the thought of when to have my second child: the traditional lifestyle was firmly ingrained in me. I welcomed my second child, Janelle Christine, in June 1990, and my third child, Rebecca Lynne, in February 1992.

Super Woman

I wasn't extraordinary. Almost every young woman I knew from my generation was doing the same thing. We all worked, married young, had our children young, and a few of us went to school to work toward earning degrees at the same time. I don't remember any of us complaining. We were blending a traditional life of what was expected of a woman—to get married and have children—and combining it with having a career, earning money, and striving to be on an equal footing with men.

One day, it hit me like a semitrailer truck that I wasn't Super Woman. I had three children, all under the age of seven; I dutifully attended college classes at night, worked almost a forty-hour week every week, shuttled children daily to school and sitters, helped my children with their homework in the evenings, and did my own until the early hours of morning. When I think back to that time today, and how I had to juggle it all, I wonder how I did it. Actually, at that time, I didn't think about all this in any negative way: I just did it because it was what I chose to do.

Back then, most husbands and fathers didn't help with housework and child-rearing responsibilities as much as they tend to today. Having men "chip in" and help was just beginning to be talked about in the parenting and working mother magazines. And mostly, women didn't ask for help (at least the women I knew).

After years of pushing myself to my limit regarding time and energy, with very little left for myself, cracks started to appear in the veneer of my marriage, and it eventually fell apart. The Enjoli commercial had *lied.* The dream shifted, and reality took its place.

Forty-some years later, I can say many women of my generation were unintentionally misled down the path of being told we could be Super Woman, Super Mom, and Super Wife all at the same time. The Enjoli perfume commercial had sold us. "The promise was 'The eight-hour perfume for the 24-hour woman.'"[33] But no one really knew it couldn't all be done at the same time because this was new territory women were exploring.

Change and Challenge

Then one day a new door opened for me. Someone who wanted to buy our business approached my father. After three years of back and forth negotiations, my father, and the other shareholders (David, Patty, and me) finally agreed to the sale of the company.

I picked up and moved my life to the Chicago area after a three-year, long-distance courtship with the man who is now my husband. We married in May 2002, the same month my family sold our company. While my son decided to stay in Pennsylvania, my two daughters soon joined me in Chicago. I decided to pursue an executive MBA (master of business administration) at Lake Forest Graduate School of Management, Lake Forest, Illinois. After four years of rigorous study, I received my MBA in June 2007, graduating valedictorian, with my husband, father, daughters, uncle David, and stepmother watching from the front row in The Crystal Gardens Ballroom on Chicago's Navy Pier. I was told after the graduation ceremony that my father was so proud of me he couldn't stop crying and everyone almost ran out of tissues.

To say that selling the company, remarrying, and moving from a quaint city in Pennsylvania to an urban area near the big city of Chicago was a seamless transition would be a false statement. This was one of the most challenging periods of my life. I left behind family and everything that was familiar to me. The emotional safety net that my father had created by providing a secure job for me was gone.

The plans that I had made, and the vision I had about how things were going to be and flow in this move to start a new beginning, didn't work out as perfectly as I had planned them in my mind. But I eventually found my footing, thanks to all my father taught me and all I learned while I worked alongside him.

Because I had such an incredible experience and know what it is like to work in a great manufacturing organization, today, when I meet someone who runs their own manufacturing company, I admit that I sometimes feel a slight twinge of loss. I think about the employees who used to work for our business and how they were all like family to us. The metal and plastic components they machined were like art: precision-machined to our customers' exact requirements, and incredibly beautiful. What if we hadn't sold the company? What future opportunities that may have existed for the family did we pass up? Which of my children would be helping me run the business today if we had retained ownership of the company? But then I see my children doing an excellent job of creating productive lives on their own, with me being in the background cheering them on for every little success! I acknowledge that selling the company freed me up to pursue other interests and a different life path—one that I enjoy tremendously.

I loved the manufacturing business that my father and my family created. When I travel to Florida to visit my uncle David and my sister Patty, our conversations quickly turn toward our shared family experiences of working at the shop together in our family business. We share memories and tell stories, talking mostly about my father and the deep admiration we had for him. Unequivocally, we all agree it was one of the best times of our lives.

Closing Words

The manufacturing industry has changed and welcomes women much more than it did when I first started. My closing piece of advice to young women is no matter what type of career you choose, seek a mentor who will help guide you. I acknowledge that not everyone gets to have a Jerry Troutman in their life. And I was fortunate to have two great mentors. Yet I am confident that there are great mentors out there, and if you look for them, you will find them. My father was the most influential mentor in my life, and the generous attention he gave to me made all the difference in my career and quality of life. It does not matter if your mentor is a man or a woman.

Put these questions in the forefront of your mind when you are seeking employment:

Are there opportunities to have a mentor and be taken under someone else's wing in order to help you succeed?

Are there strong female role models visible at many, if not all, levels in the organization—from the CEO/president level, to middle management, to the production floor?

Are there mentorship or apprenticeship programs in place?

The answers to these questions will indicate if a supportive, female-friendly environment exists.

Also, think about how you want to shape your life and the roles you want to play. Do you want to be a worker, have a professional career, be a CEO, wife, or mother? What is it that you want to do? What do you want the timing of these roles in your life to be? As a woman you can have it all—just not all at once.

For any job, consider if there are family-friendly policies that support women (and their families) at the times in their lives when they might need them most, such as when having and raising children or caring for aging parents. It is pragmatic to consider these things even in the early stages of your career.

Talk to women who work in and own manufacturing companies, like the ones in this book, to find out what jobs are available, what the pay scale is, and what career opportunities for long-term growth are available. Visit and tour companies that make products you like to use. Look for a company that hires skilled labor, uses advanced technologies, and is forward thinking.

Manufacturing is still an open frontier, one that women are still exploring. Young women today have so many opportunities, even more than my generation did. If you decide to pursue a career in manufacturing, you will be more readily accepted than women were when I began working in the industry.

As women, we have the opportunity to lead extraordinarily rich lives. We can have a career, become a wife, a mother, and we have an earning potential that our mothers, grandmothers, and great-grandmothers could not have imagined.

My generation sought the dream of feminine perfection. We made mistakes and learned some hard lessons, which is what societal progress and evolution are about. Enduring change is made one step at a time, and it takes time. We are all recipients of the lessons learned and actions taken by countless women who have come before us.

I hope you enjoy reading the many stories in this book about women who are leaders, and found fulfilling, meaningful careers in manufacturing.

• • •

***CNC (Computer Numerical Control) Precision Machining** A process used in manufacturing that involves the use of computers to control machinery that makes complicated patterns and shapes in a highly automated way, and with a high degree of repeatable accuracy.

Precision Hard Chrome Plating A chromic-acid-based coating that is put on metals that is corrosion-resistant and has a low coefficient of friction ("drag").

Plastic Stamping A manufacturing method that uses a high-speed punch press with tooling and dies that enable a shape to be punched out of a strip of plastic.

Janet Kaiser

Title: CEO	**Title:** President
Company: Ex-Cell Kaiser Manufacturing & Design	**Company:** Century Metal Spinning Company
Location: Franklin Park, Illinois	**Location:** Bensenville, Illinois
Manufacturing Processes: Proprietary, Powder Coating*	**Manufacturing Processes:** CNC Precision Metal Spinning, CNC Precision Machining, Precision Metal Stamping*
Industries Served: Recycling, Hospitality, Facility Management	**Industries Served:** Aerospace, Defense, Industrial, Commercial, and Ex-Cell Kaiser
Examples of Products Made: Waste and recycling receptacles, dustpans, hospitality carts.	**Examples of Products Made:** Components for aerospace, defense, industrial, and other commercial applications; Ex-Cell Kaiser's products.
Employees: 45–50	**Employees:** 25

Personal Interests: Art, reading books (business, biography), and learning to speak French

• • •

A Woman of Substance

A woman of substance is a woman of power and positive influence, and someone who lives her life with meaning. In manufacturing circles, when I mentioned to people that I interviewed Janet Kaiser for this book, their voices took on a reverent tone while they expressed to me their deep admiration for her skills, personal character, and accomplishments in the industry. Janet grew up at a time in the manufacturing industry when there weren't many women taking part. A trailblazer for young women in manufacturing today, many people acknowledge that Janet is someone to pay close attention to.

Janet owns and operates two companies. She is CEO of Ex-Cell Kaiser Manufacturing & Design (since 2007), and she is the president of Century Metal Spinning Company (since 1979). When I met her, she seemed to be a rather reserved. I had the sense she was a woman of few words who didn't value idle chitchat. After all, she is a busy woman running two of her own businesses. So, I dove right into opening our interview. It took only a few minutes for her to reveal the fascinating story of her family's decades-long history in manufacturing. I was delighted that she had opened up and was so generous with sharing details.

Janet's grandfather established Ex-Cell Kaiser Manufacturing & Design (formerly Ex-Cell Metal Products) in 1933. Throughout the company's history, there has been a line of family succession that has spanned three generations. Her grandfather passed the business on to her father. Her father passed the business on to her brother who later passed it on to Janet. This is remarkable as Joseph Astrachan, PhD, past editor at the *Family Business Review*, notes: "More than 30% of all family-owned businesses survive into the second generation. Twelve percent will still be viable into the third generation, with 3% of all family businesses operating at the fourth-generation level and beyond."[34]

Janet told me it is deeply rewarding to her to honor the company's history and the family members who came before her.

She's now been in business for almost forty years and clearly possesses an abundance of wisdom from this experience. After earning a bachelor's degree in fine arts, she became involved in the family business to keep the legacy of the business intact.

She toiled running Century, her first business, by day, and attending a technical school at night to study shop math, CAD (Computer-Aided Design), and how to operate precision lathes and milling machines.

When she took over Ex-Cell in 2007 from her brother, it was in dire financial straits. She did this because she wanted to carry on the legacy of the business that her grandfather had started, and as a way to honor all of her family's hard work over decades that had gone into building the business. She applied herself to mastering the skills that leading two manufacturing businesses demanded.

Janet is a woman who stirs my soul because we share a related background of going to college and studying art and ending up learning how to interpret blueprints and run a machine lathe—a machine that holds and rotates a workpiece to perform various machining operations, such as turning and drilling—on the shop floor. One would assume the disciplines of art and the machining of metals are separate from one another, but they are not. Machining is both an art and science. There is an art to holding a piece of metal or plastic and machining it to a shape, and a science to maintaining the part (or component) within the engineer's specified measurements and tolerances it needs to be so that the part fits exactly into the assembly where it needs to go.

Janet was generous with her time and took me on a tour of the Ex-Cell Kaiser plant. Overlooking the plant floor from the mezzanine provided me with the sense of being a visionary. In their product showroom I saw an array of colorful indoor and outdoor waste receptacles, dustpans, and food service carts. All were sturdy and impressive. From my background in precision machining, I could see that these were well-designed, finely machined, high-quality products. As she escorted me around the brightly lit room, Janet told me about the history of each product and how it came to be.

From our hour together, I discovered Janet is a wise, intelligent woman who leads people with integrity and heart. She strives to make a difference in the lives of the people who work for her, and those she mentors, to help them flourish in the manufacturing industry.

Her message to young women thinking about a career in manufacturing is to learn how to be assertive and confident. Know what you want. Stand up for yourself. Develop a technical knowledge base so you know what you're talking about.

Janet is a remarkable example of how manufacturing can provide a great career opportunity to women. She is an inspiration and role model for young women anywhere. You can do whatever it is you wish to do and create a meaningful life.

• • •

What's your story? How did you get to where you are today, being CEO of Ex-Cell Kaiser and the president of Century Spinning?

My grandfather started Ex-Cell. He was a motion picture projector operator back in the day and worked in movie theaters. He was a technical person. Motion picture projector operators were considered engineers at the time. He worked with lighting, projectors, and then made products for the hallways, foyers, and entranceways for the theaters in Chicago. He started with stand urns, dustpans, and products such as that.

My dad later took over the business and ran it for about fifty years. The products evolved. Then my brother led the business for a while, and the products further evolved into adding waste receptacles—the major product line that we manufacture and carry today.

When I took over the business ten years ago it was in dire financial straits. I got involved and decided it was worth saving. It was a big decision. There were many things involved. But we all wound up bringing the company back.

I started Century Metal Spinning Company in 1979. This company was a vendor for Ex-Cell Kaiser. The owner was retiring and selling the business. We took over the business and ran it alongside Ex-Cell.

What is your background? How did you prepare to own two manufacturing businesses?

I went to college and got a bachelor's degree in fine arts. Then I went back to night school at Triton College in their industrial trades department. I took many machine shop and CAD (*Computer-Aided Design*) courses.

I got my technical training by going to school at night and working during the day. That's what got me up to speed with what I was doing at Century Metal Spinning, which we still run today.

Did you have any mentors?

Yes, my father was my mentor on the business side of things. My teachers at Triton College were great. There was a good shop math teacher there and other shop teachers for different classes. They were very helpful. There was one other woman in the classes. Otherwise, it was pretty much me as the only woman.

As I got more involved in running the business, I joined two manufacturing organizations, the TMA (*Technology and Manufacturing Association*), a local organization, and PMA (*Precision Metalforming Association*), a national organization.

I served on a board of TMA for a term and was the only woman on the board. Since then there have been more women. There was one who preceded me. The men in the industry were mostly very welcoming, engaging, and willing to teach—inviting me to go visit their shops and share their best practices. That's what organizations like that do.

My mentors were people I got to know in business, and who either took me under their wing or I picked their brain. Being married at the time, my husband was involved in these organizations, too. Occasionally, I became associated with my husband's business. People didn't realize I had my own businesses. So, that was funny . . . that people just assumed things (*that she was there only as the wife of a manufacturing company business owner and not as an owner of businesses herself*).

Do you believe manufacturing is a practical career choice for women?

Yes. In today's world, manufacturing is changing. We hear how it's hard to find skilled labor. The skills required will be at a higher level in the engineering and technical end of things, whether it's programming for automation, for robotics, or design work in CAD. Here at Ex-Cell, our director of operations is a woman. She has a technical background and comes from the same era as me.

Our vice president of sales and marketing at Ex-Cell is a woman. Over at Century, some of my key people are women. Manufacturing is alive and well. It's not the same as it used to be. There are positions, whether in design, engineering for programming, logistics, purchasing, and materials management; there are many job positions within an organization.

Are there opportunities for women to rise to different positions within the company?

Certainly, especially in my world of smaller, family-owned businesses. In larger corporate environments like we deal with here, we've seen women shift to different positions within those larger companies. There's definitely the opportunity for movement. The more you know, the more valuable you will be.

What do you believe are the three biggest misconceptions about women who work in/have careers in manufacturing?

There will always be assumptions about what kind of positions women have in manufacturing. I think this is changing.

I never got bogged down [when] dealing with the men in the industry. You need to know your stuff. You need to know what you're talking about. I've been in many meetings where I'm at a table surrounded by a bunch of male engineers, like at Lockheed (*an aircraft manufacturer*). That's shifted. There are now more female engineers around the table.

What advancements do you see happening in manufacturing over the next five years that will create opportunities for people who are considering a career in manufacturing?

I think technical careers are changing. You could be a programmer and create files to run machinery—where you create the files in one station and then transfer them to the machine that makes a part. There's 3-D printing coming along, so you need to know metallurgy, and about the changes in and uses of materials. You could have a technical or engineering background—whether it's chemical and on the testing side of materials versus mechanical and working with materials and their properties.

What resources would you recommend to young women (or even their parents) who are considering a career in manufacturing to help them learn more?

There are more engineering programs in schools today where they hold classes for young women and their parents. They spend a day and break into small groups. The girls take part in different activities. Some are academic-related where they'll go through the use of math in the industry. But other ones, to my surprise, were about assertiveness. Workshops were being done on how to speak up, how to explain yourself, how to introduce yourself, how to become confident, and how not to get bullied or put down.

There are engineering camps that are girl or female-centric—where it's all women. It makes for an easier time, working together and collaborating, as opposed to what happens at that age with boys and girls. I think it's important that boys and girls integrate into a coed environment, so the boys get used to girls—and the girls get used to boys on a more professional level.

Why do you think manufacturing is a good career choice for young women?

It's good pay. It must interest you in how things are made and what makes things work. If you have an interest in those things, and the more engineering background you get across different spectrums, the higher the wage you can demand. You can always go into business for yourself.

At Century, we do contract manufacturing and make custom-to-print to our customers' specifications (*which describes the requirements and quality to which a product should conform).* Sometimes there is an engineering intermediary. More companies are outsourcing their engineering to these types of operations where there's a group of engineers who have gotten together and started their own company. They become an independent engineering resource for a large corporation. There are many facets to this whole arena of how things are being made.

What's your number one piece of advice to young women (and their parents) who are considering a career in manufacturing?

You must figure out what you're good at doing. For young people, you're evolving, you're developing, so you don't know yet what floats your boat. So just getting this exposure and get as broad a background as you can (*to find out what you like, want, and are good at doing*), in your community, at school, in clubs, whatever. Find what piques your interest at an earlier age. Build upon that. One thing leads to another. You may start somewhere, but you may end up somewhere completely different. It's a matter of exposing yourself to many things.

What is the personal return on investment you get from leading your businesses? How does it nourish your soul?

It is challenging and satisfying at the same time working with the different personalities at high levels, at managerial levels, at other levels. It takes a certain personality to run a sales department. It takes a certain technical personality to run operations. It takes a certain personality to understand and run the finance part of the business.

Trying to blend those different personalities and create a team is challenging because everybody comes at it from a different angle, and they don't always understand the other person's perspective. It's become more fun for me at this point. And when we have a challenging job, it's very satisfying when we conclude that job.

Collaborating with the customers at Century Metal Spinning, we're often collaborating at an engineering level, whether it's with rocket scientists or others. You're sitting down at the table with those people, and it's always interesting. And fun. You learn a lot. And I enjoy that I'm carrying on the family tradition. That's very much in the back of my mind—that there are family members who preceded me.

Why do you care about getting more women involved in manufacturing?

Because I'm a woman. I've enjoyed the people who've seen me as a mentor. And now I feel like I'm looking at them as mentors, because I see them making their own way, and it's like, "Oh, I need to stay in touch with the younger generation." Seeing their success is very heartening. And they are working to spread the word to more women about a career in manufacturing. It's so satisfying to see that, and I hope to see a lot more of it.

What haven't we talked about that you want people to know?

Speaking as someone in the business, and who's been at it for a while, I've seen the business evolve over the years. You find out what you like to do, and what you're good at doing. Then you must hire other people to do the things that either you don't want to do, or they're better at doing them than you are.

For young women coming into the field, your ideal job may not be as a business owner, but maybe working for someone else. You must know what you're talking about, so you can compete head-to-head. It's a matter of knowing your stuff and asserting yourself at the right time, and in the right places.

And you can't let yourself get discouraged or ruminate about "woe is me" if things don't go according to your plan. You must pick yourself up and dust yourself off. There's a saying I heard on a radio program about a woman who was a principal at a school that wasn't in a well-off community. She came from that background, and one thing she would do every morning was get on the intercom and say, "If nobody told you they loved you today, I'm telling you I love you." And if they ever came up with excuses and reasons not to do something, or something hit them the wrong way, she would say, "So what? Now what?"

So, don't ruminate about it. Stop "looping about it" as we say in my family. You get on with it. Learn from it. You could spend an enormous amount of time wallowing and not moving ahead with your career or your life. Or you can keep building your personal capital. Keep building upon it. I came from a strong family background. To me, that's influential.

CAREER ACTIVITIES

What do you think it was like to be a woman in manufacturing in the 1970s? In what ways do you think it is different for women today?

Janet got a degree in fine arts and then learned how to do machining. What does her education and career path tell you about the ways of making career choices?

What can young women do to increase their own confidence and assertiveness?

What does Janet recommend young women do to learn about what interests them to find out what they might like to do, or go for, in their future careers?

• • •

***CNC (Computer Numerical Control) Precision Metal Spinning** A process of turning (spinning) a flat piece of metal on a lathe around a pattern allowing the metal to form to a desired shape. Metal spinning is used when there is a need for a three dimensional shape (e.g., hemispheres, cones) to be formed from a single piece of material.

CNC (Computer Numerical Control) Precision Machining A process used in manufacturing that involves the use of computers to control machinery that makes complicated patterns and shapes in a highly automated way, and with a high degree of repeatable accuracy.

Precision Metal Stamping A process of converting a flat piece of metal into various shapes by using a tool and die surface. Common metal stamping operations are piercing, bending, embossing, and progressive stamping, where multiple dies are used to make a part.

Powder Coating A dry finishing process that is harder and more durable than liquid paint. Powder coatings are resistant to impact, moisture, chemicals, ultraviolet light, and extreme weather conditions, which makes them scratch, chip, abrasion, and corrosion resistant. Powder coating is available in an almost limitless range of textures and colors.

Cynthia Campos

Title: Set-Up Apprentice

Company: Smith & Richardson, Inc.

Location: Geneva, Illinois

Manufacturing Processes: CNC Precision Machining, Precision Metal Stamping, Precision Slide-Forming*

Industries Served: Aerospace, Medical, Casting, Sports/Recreation, Transportation, and other various industries

Examples of Products Made: Components for force and vibration sensors that are used on aircraft to measure braking torque and force and in-flight controls; components in meters that help measure the flow of liquids and gases; triggers on cross bows and other pieces for the sports industry.

Number of Employees: 51

Personal Interests: Metal, science, and learning technical things

• • •

For the Love of Metal

Within thirty seconds of meeting Cynthia Campos, you learn that she has a passion for metal. With a glint in her eye, she wasted no time in telling me how much she loves the science of metals and how their scientific properties fascinate her: how they can be in a solid form, melted into a glowing hot liquid, and then formed and hardened into a different shape.

Her interest in metals and science inspired her to choose a career in the metalworking industry. She feels there's an enormous opportunity for women to have a career in manufacturing, and she thinks more women need to look at the industry and give it a try. She believes passionately in pursuing your heart's desire, and to go after the career that you choose—even if your parents seek to dissuade you not to, which was Cynthia's experience.

Cynthia is a remarkable example of an independent and strong young woman. She chose her career by following her interests and passion, and she experiences personal fulfillment in making things that she believes are important and have meaning in the world.

Cynthia told me that she was the only girl in her high school machine shop class. This fact underscores how few women consider the skilled trades as a career choice. The reasons for this range from women not being informed of what manufacturing is all about to shying away from it because of the stigma of its not being a "feminine" or "culturally correct" career for women. Many young women (and men) are being discouraged from seeking a career in manufacturing by well-meaning parents who either have misconceptions about, or don't realize the career opportunities available in, the manufacturing industry.

As more women like Cynthia join the field of manufacturing, business owners will realize that women have the extraordinary skills and intelligence that match well with the technological aspects of manufacturing and other STEM-related jobs. As I talked with Cynthia, I was mesmerized and taken in by her exuberance and passion for metal and manufacturing! I hope you will be, too. It was a joy to get to know Cynthia.

• • •

Cynthia, what is your position here at Smith & Richardson?

I'm a set-up apprentice. I help set up and run the machines for a job.

When you were in high school, did you take part in the vocational training programs?

Yes, I took two years of precision manufacturing in high school. Year one was all about the manual lathes, mills, and the grinder and other stuff. Year two we got into CNC (*Computer Numerical Control machines*). From those classes, I ended up with two CNC certifications: I got my CNC lathe operator certification, and I got my job planning, bench block, and layout certification.

How did you choose this career?

I've always had a fascination with metal. I thought it was cool. I grew up watching cartoons sometimes, but mostly, documentaries. The science of metal always intrigued me—that it can create so many things. So, when I got into high school, I told them, "I really like metal. Is there something I can do with this interest?" And my guidance counselor took me to the metal shop. I never looked back.

What's your favorite material?

I like cobalt steel. It's nice! When I look in the shop, sometimes I'll see different metals, like pH (*stainless steel*), and I'm like, "I could study that. That might be a new favorite."

What's your favorite thing to do at work?

I like setting up. I think it's so cool to start the process. It's easier operating [a machine] because you push the "Go" button, and you check the parts. Yet to get your hands in a machine, to set up the tooling right, then running that first part, and seeing it's good, or close to good, it feels like such an accomplishment; you have to set up as fast as you can, but as correctly as possible.

Do you have mentors at the company?

Yes, I have my mentor who trains me. He's only here two and a half days a week. So, for the other two days, everyone takes turns mentoring me. They'll check with me, "Hey, how ya doing?" I'll be like, "I'm good. My parts are great."

Are the men that work here supportive of you? Do they want to help you?

Yes, it's a great work environment. It's like a mini family here at work.

Do you believe manufacturing is a good career choice for women?

Yes, I feel like it's a great career for women because there are not so many people doing the same thing—people have different jobs, so it helps you to find a strength. There are so many ways you can grow, and you're not stuck somewhere, you know? You could switch around and run many types of machines, which makes it great.

One of the other guys showed me the wire (*an EDM machine that cuts material using a thin, electrically-charged wire*), which I didn't realize we had. He explained it, and I'm like, "Dude, I like setting up, but I feel like it'd be fun to run this one, too." I'll run a machine or set up. I'm available. There is so much room to do many things, it's freeing. I know my parents were against it having a career in manufacturing because they thought it was a bad type of job.

Why didn't your parents think manufacturing was a good career choice?

They thought of it being more like working in a warehouse. My dad, he works with machines, but he talks about it like it's a dirty kind of place or rundown. It's so incredible [manufacturing] that it hurts me that there aren't many women or young people in the trades.

Do you think part of why your parents discouraged you is because they didn't realize how great of a career it can be?

Yes, I feel like that is it. As you mentioned, even counselors back in the day, and now, still push for college. They'll mention trade school, but they'll take on a lower tone, and speak a lot quicker, so it passes by your ear.

What types of jobs are available for women at Smith & Richardson?

I'd let them know there are machine operators and set-up people. We have engineers, too. They could also work in quality control. There's also the stamping department. I'm not sure what all the different job titles are. We have a shipping department, too. It's a huge company.

If women know they want to be here, there's room for them. I can't remember how many people we have in this company itself—I believe it's around fifty people, we have plenty of room for more people. And you make something (*parts*) that goes into important things in the world.

What do you believe are the three biggest misconceptions women have about working in/having a career in manufacturing?

That it's more of a man-dominated place. How there isn't any room for women. Or they can't do the job as well as a man. But that's anywhere (*a common attitude in the workplace across the United States*). Just because I'm a woman doesn't mean you can't give me as high a standard as you give a man. I feel like that's an enormous misconception.

Or people say, "Oh, women can't do a good job. They don't want to get dirty," or something like that. If you're more girly, I can see you not wanting to chip a nail or get oil on you. But I grew up with people who like to be grease monkeys, so a little dirt on me doesn't bother me.

What advancements do you see happening in manufacturing over the next five years that will create opportunities for people who are considering a career in manufacturing?

I think new technologies. I think making more intricate parts, which will be fun. Out on the shop floor, I saw this cool thing that reminded me of the DNA strands, which looked . . . I mean, if we will end up building more extreme things, then our machinery will advance, too.

If we get more intricate, more advanced, our skill level will grow with that. Once one thing goes up, it creates a domino effect, and it expands things. With new technology, there are always new skills to learn.

What resources would you recommend to young women (or even their parents) who are considering a career in manufacturing to help them learn more?

They could go online to do research, look at things. I'm sure by now some companies have an online tour of their place—you know, like many colleges have.

If they know people who work in manufacturing, I suggest talking to them to get an insider's point of view.

You mentioned that the company is paying for you to attend school . What textbooks are you reading?

One is about the math behind manufacturing. We get into calculating speeds, feeds, and surface area. I have another one that goes into detail about blueprints. It's technical reading. I like it. It's really great!

All that geometry and trigonometry . . . It starts to make sense, doesn't it?

It makes me happy because math and science were my highest grades ever in high school. I always get a grade of 99 percent or 100 percent without my trying. I helped more boys in math and science than there were girls that needed help.

We must get this message out. That's what we're doing here. Girls are good at science. Girls are good at math. We're technical.

Cynthia, why do you think manufacturing is a good career choice for women?

It is a good career. Smith & Richardson, they're paying for my education. I don't have to pay any of my own money to attend TMA (*Technology and Manufacturing Association*) or my online classes, so I get a free education. I get educated while working, and I'm getting paid for it. By the time I finish my schooling, I could be making as much as someone who went to college for eight years. Without all the debt. That's great!

What's your number one piece of advice to young women (and their parents) who are considering a career in manufacturing?

My piece of advice would be take the risk. You won't ever achieve anything if you're always worrying about things.

I'm leading on a path. I feel great. I did that in high school, too, because I was the first: I was the only girl in my manufacturing class. I was the first one ever.

Was your instructor in high school supportive?

Yes, he supported me. I think he was excited to finally get a girl in there.

Why do you care about getting more women involved in manufacturing?

I care because I feel like it'd be a nice change for something new, you know? Like you mentioned, most of the women that you interviewed didn't plan on a career in manufacturing. I feel like if we make a push for more women, they'd be like me: they'd want to come. It gives you a reason to wake up in the morning if you love what you're doing.

At Smith & Richardson, there are heavy materials, fixtures, and things like that that you have to move around. Does this hold women back?

No. Sure, it might take you an extra minute (*to get the raw materials you need to the machines you're setting up or running*). We have machines that help lift pallets. I've seen guys carry two, three, and more metal bars. And then I'll look at what I'm carrying, and I'll have two extra metal bars than him. I'm like, "Yeah!"

If you need a little help, then you ask for it. If you need to carry a little less, then you do that. Time efficiency is important. But make sure you don't hurt yourself. Because if you hurt yourself, then we're out of hands. Then who will help someone else lift something?

What haven't we talked about that you want people to know?

For women or any young person, even if your family doesn't support your decision to go into manufacturing, as long as you end up being your own number one cheerleader or number one fan, if you know what you want, then go for it. You need to be comfortable with who you are, and you've got to trust your own choices. Don't be a doctor because your mother said so. If you want to be a machinist, go for it. That's what I want to end off with because that took me a while to learn.

CAREER ACTIVITIES

Cynthia is incredibly interested in and passionate about metal. What things are you excited and passionate about? How might your interests be expressed in a manufacturing career?

Do you enjoy learning technical subjects, such as math, science, and how to design and make things out of raw materials?

Does it bother Cynthia that she doesn't work in a place with a lot of other women? Why or why not? What do you think about that? How do you think about it for yourself—will it matter or not and why?

Why does Cynthia think that manufacturing is a good career choice for women? What does she suggest you do or think about if your family members, or other people, don't support your decision to explore manufacturing as a potential career?

• • •

***CNC (Computer Numerical Control) Precision Machining** A process used in manufacturing that involves the use of computers to control machinery that makes complicated patterns and shapes in a highly automated way, and with a high degree of repeatable accuracy.

Precision Metal Stamping A process of converting a flat piece of metal into various shapes by using a tool and die surface. Common metal stamping operations are piercing, bending, embossing, and progressive stamping, where multiple dies are used to make a part.

Precision Slide-Forming A metal stamping process that combines the progressive die process, which consists of several individual workstations, each of which performs one or more different operations on the part. The ability to produce components in this way allows for the possibility of performing multiple cutting and/or forming operations simultaneously.

Patricia Miller

Title: CEO + Visionary

Company: Matrix4

Location: Woodstock, Illinois

Manufacturing Process: Plastic Injection Molding*

Industries Served: Cosmetics, Automotive, Household Appliances, Healthcare, and others

Examples of Products Made: Components for laundry machines and refrigerators, cosmetic packaging, hammers and other industrial tools, and almost anything that is made of plastic

Number of Employees: 50

Personal Interests: Reading, personal growth, dancing, working and playing hard

• • •

Chart Your Path

In the fall of 2017, I attended a manufacturing conference near Chicago. In a panel discussion about robotics and automation, one of the panelists was a young woman. She talked about her company, Matrix4, and the circumstances around how she came to buy the business, the investments she had made in robotics to boost productivity and efficiency, and how she identified an issue within the company culture and then deconstructed and rebuilt it to create the type of company culture she desired.

Paying attention to company culture is a priority for many of the female business owners I interviewed. So, what does culture mean when it comes to business? Think of it this way: just like people have personalities, so do companies. Culture makes up the personality of a company and includes a variety of elements, such as core values, the company's mission or "purpose for being," the work environment (e.g., creative, innovative, or more rule-bound), and how the people within the company conduct themselves on a day-to-day basis in interactions between fellow employees, customers, and the community at large.

I marveled at her triumphs, knowing myself how hard they can be to achieve. And when she said that she didn't have a manufacturing background, my mind whirled with questions: How did she get to where she is now having had no manufacturing experience? How did she wind up purchasing and turning around a failing manufacturing business? And why did she want to? I absolutely wanted to learn more about her story. At the end of the event, I asked Patricia if I could interview her to publish her story in my blog. I was delighted when she enthusiastically agreed.

On the day of Patricia's interview, I parked my car across the street from Matrix4's red-brown brick building, and noticed it was set high enough up on a grassy bank from the curb that I couldn't gain a glimpse of the place inside the windows. As I walked into the lobby, the space projected the image of a start-up company with a feisty attitude. What particularly caught my eye was the signage on the wall: hand-painted, white and black wooden letters (like the kind you find in craft stores) that gleamed from gold glitter paint and spelled out the phrase "Matrix4 Makes Things in PLASTIC Meaningfully That Matter." In an instant, I knew I was in a high-energy, "techy," and fun environment . . . and that a woman was clearly running this place.

It wasn't long before a slim woman in white fur boots was striding toward me. Patricia is the fresh face of manufacturing today: youthful, hip, confident, and wickedly smart. Meeting her begs you to alter your mind about what you think about manufacturing and the people who work in it.

I learned that before Patricia became involved in manufacturing, she had political ambitions and had received an MA in public policy from University College London (UCL). After working in politics for three years, she set off for the jet-setting scene of the adrenaline-fueled biotech industry, traveling the world to launch new brands.

So how, and why, did Patricia choose to become the CEO of Matrix4?

It turns out the company was founded by Patricia's grandfather, who was a toolmaker by trade. During a trip home to Chicago in the spring of 2014 to visit her family, Patricia discovered that her grandfather was in ill health, and the business was in a challenging place. The preceding recession had hit the company hard, and it had never recovered. The business was losing about $100,000 every month, operating at ten percent capacity, and faced closing its doors by year-end.

Patricia dedicated herself to helping her grandfather and bought the business from him. She moved back to Chicago in 2014 and committed herself to rebuilding the organization with the same focus and passion her grandfather had when he established the company in 1978.

Patricia's accomplishments are inspiring and nothing short of astounding to me. Here is a young woman, who had no background in manufacturing (which is supposed to be a "tough," male-dominated industry), who made the many and right decisions that needed to be made to turn the business financially around. That is, and would be, a challenging task for even the most seasoned and experienced professionals who have worked in the manufacturing industry for decades. Patricia represents, and is, the "new face" of manufacturing, and she is a role model to other young women for what it looks like to be part of the manufacturing industry and the contemporary "makers movement," a societal movement that embodies a creative, innovation-driven, artisanal spirit, and creates an opportunity to spark a revival in the manufacturing industry. Patricia is a shining example—gold glitter and all—of how it can be for young women in the industry.

• • •

Patricia, what is your background?

I have a Bachelor of Arts in journalism and mass communications, a BBA (bachelor of business administration) in marketing and entrepreneurship from the University of Iowa, a master of arts in public policy from UCL (University College London), a market research certificate from the University of Georgia, and I went through the leadership program at Eli Lilly and Company.

I started out in politics at Labour Party Headquarters in London with the [then] prime minister, Tony Blair, and earned a graduate degree in legal and political theory at the University College London, England. From there I served as a [U.S.] state senate political aide in Hawaii.

Then I went from politics to the biotech industry, building and launching new brands. At Eli Lilly, I worked with teams and launched six new drugs, and worked in market research and brand development for several brands in disease states, such as neuroscience, diabetes, and men's health. I did that for ten years.

Then I moved on to a start-up biotech company in San Diego, California, and focused on business development and commercialization of the company's assets for two years before deciding to return to the Chicago area. It was an exciting time. But I was ready to get off a jet plane and do something meaningful in a different way.

What professional organizations do you currently take part in?

I'm a board member of NAM (*the National Association of Manufacturers, a manufacturing advocacy group*), Centegra Health System, and mHub Chicago (*a product and manufacturing innovation center*). I'm also an advisory board member for the University of Iowa's John Pappajohn Entrepreneurial Alumni Advisory Board, and Prairie Ridge High School Incubator Program (*a program that helps start-up companies to develop by providing space to operate and receive business management training*).

How do you find the time to do all this?

If I enjoy it, and find value in taking part, and have the time, I have no problem fitting it into my schedule. I like to keep myself heavily engaged in the industry.

How did you get to where you are today, leading Matrix4?

I was launching brands and moved nine times over the span of ten years from London to China to New York City to San Diego . It was a fast-paced, exciting time and took adrenaline to keep running at 100 miles per hour. I traveled a lot. I loved spending time in Hawaii.

In May 2014, I flew to Chicago to attend a conference. While there, I took the time to visit family. When I was driving out of the city into the suburbs, I noticed many businesses were closed down and thought the area looked depressed compared to where I came from [San Diego]. The area wasn't thriving; it was struggling to recover from the economic downturn.

My grandfather owned Matrix4, but his health was deteriorating. My grandmother didn't know how to run the business; it was failing. I learned more about the business's struggles after my grandmother let me see the company's financials.

There was no succession plan in place. I took over the business and had to figure out how to stop the bleeding of cash and pivot to turn the business around. It was mid-2014 when I moved back to Chicago and took over my grandfather's business.

Every year on December 31st, I reflect on the past year, what happened, and then decide what my goals are and what I want to do the next year. I pay attention to what comes up for me. I like to be challenged.

Turning the business around would be a big challenge. I thought about buying the business, but I wanted to determine the viability of the operation. I contacted friends who worked at McKinsey & Company (*a business consulting firm*) and asked them to look at the business, the trends, and if it was possible to turn the business around. They analyzed and determined that it was viable and thought it could be turned around. In July 2014, I left the biotech space and San Diego, moved to Chicago, and came up with a strategy and started with six people. I now have fifty employees.

When I was a little girl, I came into this factory often enough to appreciate the smell of resin, to get excited about what was being made on the factory floor, and who was on the team to make it all work efficiently. One of those key people on the floor was my mom, who was a single parent. She led the manufacturing floor as a processor. At a young age, she taught me to chart my own path, follow my own star, and never let a preconceived ceiling or stereotype dictate [the direction of my life].

What are Matrix4's top three values?

"People First," "Make Meaningfully," and "Communicate Purposefully." We came up with our values as a team. They have meaning to everyone.

Do you believe manufacturing is a good and viable career choice for women?

I struggle with this question because I think any career is good and viable for women.

Why do you care about getting more women involved in manufacturing?

I care about manufacturing and love to see broader engagement in a segment that is a critical economic driver in the U.S. And I am excited to see how it evolves to stay relevant.

What do you think is the number one challenge for women in manufacturing?

I think in STEM classes [Science, Technology, Engineering, Math] that women don't see enough other women students in the classes that look like them, that they can relate to, and see themselves as being like them someday.

Making the right connections is also a challenge: finding someone to help you, mentor you, and introduce you to the right people who can help clear the path.

What is your number one piece of advice to young women (and their parents) who are considering a career in manufacturing?

I think it is like my advice to young men, and their parents: that manufacturing is not what they may perceive as dark, dirty, and unintelligible. It is sophisticated, interesting, and has a host of opportunities for career development and growth.

What is the personal return on investment you get from leading this business? How does it nourish your soul?

The making. The creative process of building a brand, a team, and product. Representing the industry and erasing the stigma around women not belonging in the industry. Writing the next chapter in American manufacturing.

What haven't we talked about that you want people to know?

I have not had a challenge having my team get behind my leadership and direction as a woman in manufacturing.

CAREER ACTIVITIES

What do you find interesting about Patricia's story and career path?

Do you think Patricia believed in herself and her ability to succeed? What personal qualities do you think she possesses?

What education or career goals do you want to achieve in the next twelve months? Brainstorm and write down all the goals that you come up with on a piece of paper (or whatever electronic device you are using). When you're finished, circle the two to three goals that are the most exciting to you! *Examples of goals are researching careers in your subjects of interest and choosing a career, finding an internship opportunity at a company, or learning new knowledge or technical skills.*

What is the next *one* step you can take to start movement toward accomplishing each of those exciting goals you circled? Act on it.

What personal development books would you like to read? Ideas for topics could be: goal setting, leadership, building confidence, or determining the best career for you.

• • •

***Plastic Injection Molding** A method of forming plastic pieces by heating the plastic molding material until it can flow, and then injecting that melted plastic into a mold to make a desired form.

Erica Wiegel

Title: President

Companies: ARO Metal Stamping Co.

Location: Roselle, Illinois

Manufacturing Process: Precision Metal-Stamping*

Industries Served: Automotive Housing, Aerospace, Construction, Lighting, Commercial Electrical, Insert Molding Components, Defense

Examples of Products Made: Components for heat sinks (a device that absorbs heat) in automobile engines, electrical brackets and clips, parts that require plastic to be molded around metal pieces/parts

Number of Employees: 26—about half of the employees are women

Personal: Loves animals, luxury sports cars, and setting and achieving bold goals

• • •

A Role Model for Bravery

The first thing I saw when I stepped through the doorway of Erica Wiegel's office was the array of wooden and bronze-clad plaques lined up along the floor that were mounted with media stories and awards. Not one. Not two. But so many, I couldn't count them all before sitting in the chair she offered me. She noticed my amazement and said, "I haven't had time to hang them on the wall."

This accomplished young woman, who has received accolades from her peers and other fans from various professional circles, is the president of ARO Metal Stamping Co., a business she purchased in July 2015. She is also part owner of Wiegel Tool Works, Inc., which has a newly acquired subsidiary in Italy, which will give both Wiegel Tool Works and Erica Wiegel, herself, a stronger regional presence and global footprint in the metal stamping industry.

Her story in manufacturing began at an early age. She started spending time with her father in the family's manufacturing business when she was about eight years old, playing in the office, asking her father questions about what and how products were being made, and attending meetings with the staff—the kind that occur in a normal workday to get things done. As she grew older, she worked at the business part-time on weekends, after school, and during summers. After she graduated from college in 2002 with a mechanical engineering degree, she started working at her father's company full time.

Erica has a courageous spirit and enjoys the thrill of setting bold goals for herself. With her tall stature and dark hair, she made me think of the image of Diana from ancient Rome—standing powerfully with a bow held up, bowstring pulled tight, arrow in place—who takes joy in the hunt, knowing her aim is true.

Since Erica purchased ARO, the company's revenues have tripled: they've grown from $4 million to $12 million in less than three years. This is a monumental feat for a mature manufacturing company to achieve.

Erica is an enthusiastic proponent of manufacturing. She believes the industry is an excellent career choice for women because it offers opportunities for career advancement, high-income potential, and personal growth. And with the ongoing development of technologies that support manufacturing, such as robotics, the industry's success requires a continuous stream of workers learning new and more advanced skills to operate and maintain such technology.

Choosing a career in manufacturing is often a financially savvy move. Many companies invest in and pay for training and education for their employees, which provides educational alternatives that offer a successful, debt free, and rewarding career.

It was a delight to interview Erica and learn her story. She is an excellent role model for young women and shows that having confidence, knowing what you want, and learning STEM (science, technology, engineering, math) disciplines can help you choose a career path that will remain relevant in the future.

• • •

How did you get to where you are now, leading ARO Metal Stamping?

I started young—at seven, eight years old—with my dad and his factory. It always intrigued me how much things cost. My grandma always asked, "How much did you pay for that?" My dad's mother grew up in the Depression. She was very frugal, and we always watched how much we spent on everything. With my dad, I'd always walk the aisles of the shop, and I'd ask, "How much is that tool?" And my dad would always tell me.

Ever since I was ten or twelve years old, my dad shared the revenue and [accounting] books with us [siblings]. We'd sit in on meetings. We saw what [money] was coming in, and what [money] was going out.

As I was growing up, I was doing various jobs in the company: from cleaning, to being a delivery driver, to inspecting parts, to updating engineering prints, to programming and working on the machines. I had a variety of experiences in the company before I finished college. When I graduated, I didn't know what I wanted to do. So I went into the engineering department and updated drawings.

We had a prototype department that we set up a few years back for a man that had lost his company but wanted to get back on his feet again. So, we let him bring his department into our company. One day, he quit. That day, the day he left, we had more orders than we ever had before in that department. It was my responsibility to complete the orders. These were prototype jobs: you had to develop them, create them, and make different versions of them. So, I ended up taking that department over and standardizing everything. When a customer called, I could turn something around in three, four days.

I took that department, polished it into a gem, and made it a well-organized machine. By that time, I was getting bigger and bigger orders. My name was getting out there, and I was getting to look at designs that were sketches to decide if they were even possible to make, to create, to build. I was on those first calls [with customers and engineers]. That's how I evolved to where I'm at today. I've learned the business side from my dad. Then I got engineering and mechanical experience.

Do you believe manufacturing is a practical career choice for women?

Sure. One of my employees here came here from Mexico. In high school she decided she wanted to get on a career path, so she worked here part-time in summers while she was in high school. Then she graduated high school and went to a local community college and got a computer degree. She's been working here in production for fourteen years. She's my planner and buyer.

What types of jobs are available in manufacturing for women?

This is a broad question when you think of engineering. There are 50,000 different types of companies and each one of these companies has their own specific professions.

There are operations engineers, mechanical engineers, chemical engineers, buyers, planners, managers, supervisors, quality inspectors, technicians, tool and die makers, and machine programmers, marketing and sales people, job estimators, photographers, and even camera technicians. These types of jobs are in many manufacturing facilities.

Would you say one misconception about manufacturing is, "I'm just going to work on the floor at a machine?"

Correct. The worst part is I don't think people know of how big the scope of manufacturing is. And because many of my parts go into cars, I must make sure that every single one of my parts—whether I make one or five million—that every single one of them is perfect.

I mentioned photography. A lot of moms have a limited time they can work. We have many sensors and cameras that need to get programmed. I can send files to them at home, they can work when their kids are sleeping or after school, and then send the files back. Who would think a single mom who likes photography can have a major job in the manufacturing industry?

What do you believe are the three biggest misconceptions women have about working in/having a career in manufacturing?

That it's unsafe, it's a dying trade, and low wages.

What advancements do you see happening in manufacturing over the next five years that will create opportunities for women who are considering a career in manufacturing?

Technology's gotten us here, and it's catapulted us to a whole new platform. Right now, we have mechanical arm flywheel machines (*a machine that stores rotational energy and releases it later when required*), and it's like the flywheel has to go up in a circle like this (*she lifted her arm, then rotated it in a circle to demonstrate*).

We also have server machines (*which store information that can be used by other computers*). A switch from a mechanical machine to a server machine is like a switch from a Pinto to a Ferrari.

I can take any person and train them how to run my Ferrari. Not only do I invest in this person's training so they can do the job, but this person will make a lot more money. A better part gets made, which means higher wages. It's a domino effect. I get improved machines and robots. I need to pay people more to run these machines. My Ferrari will not run forever, so now I need service technicians. There are spin-off companies that create their own technology team to send out to my company to fix these machines. This is part of the domino effect. It spreads everywhere fast.

Higher skills and wages make a better living and family environment. As technology grows, everybody will get a better paycheck and placement in life.

We often hear robots will take away jobs. What are your thoughts?

A few things. People earn money to design and make the robots. People earn money to support and program the robots. More and better things are being manufactured. It creates a domino effect of more people making more money. Robots coming more into play will take away some jobs. But these will be low-skilled, repetitive jobs.

I mean, even the technology when I came here to ARO . . . we were doing all these hand labels and stuff. Now I have fifteen computers on the floor and two fingerprint identification devices. With technology and robots, people can work on more value-added activities. It's a huge domino effect.

What resources would you recommend to young women (or even their parents) who are considering a career in manufacturing to help them learn more?

I often speak at high schools and junior highs. I not only speak to the kids, but I also speak to the [guidance] counselors, so they find out what types of jobs are out there in manufacturing.

I would tell them to call their local Chamber of Commerce because they work with manufacturers. Many companies will let people in their door to tour, things like that.

I sponsor local activities in the neighborhood—at the park districts and things like that. My logo is on their sports shirts. I'm a metal stamper. I'm an engineer. You see my company name, you look me up.

And if you call me and say, "I'm interested in the field." I'll say, "Yeah, come on over and I'll take you on a tour. Bring the family—the mom, the dad, and the kid—to come visit my shop."

If people come to your plant what are they going to see? Can you describe the experience for them?

It's like taking a farm kid and sticking them in the middle of Times Square. There's so much to see and to do. I would recommend finding a company that makes something you would enjoy seeing manufactured, so you can better relate to what the outcome is.

There's a Nestle chocolate factory. You can see them mixing all the stuff to make the chocolate and the process it has to get through, and then the molds, how they wrap the foods, how they package, and how they put it into a box, and how they ship it. You might enjoy that more than seeing me make metal parts because, by the time I make my metal part, I can tell you what it will be (*such as a thin metal shield that goes into the engine of a Ferrari*), but you don't see the final component like you would a chocolate bar.

What books do you read?

I don't read books. I am a news junkie and read it on my iPhone all the time. I must know what's happening in politics and the economy to know if I need to pump the breaks. I want to know if cash will keep coming in. When '08 and '09 hit, if you didn't have cash, you weren't king anymore. There are only a few kings left on the block. Nobody can sit here and say, "Hey, I want to duplicate Erica's shop," because that's impossible now. I mean, where do you start?**

Why do you believe manufacturing is a good career choice for young women?

Besides offering unlimited career opportunities, what I like is when I sketch something on a piece of paper it can come to life. So, for me, it's like driving. I feel a sense of satisfaction seeing a Chevy Volt because I developed some parts in that engine. There are many opportunities to advance a career in manufacturing. The best thing is with each job you learn new skills.

With manufacturing, you gain all these skills in your toolbox. You take this toolbox to whatever manufacturing job you have. You eventually end up with your own toolbox of skills.

What's your number one piece of advice to young women (and their parents) who are considering a career in manufacturing?

What's holding them back? I see nothing that should be.

Going back to 2008–2009, and even before that, we saw manufacturing jobs hemorrhaging out of the U.S. economy. That's fresh in people's minds. What are your thoughts?

In '08 and '09 what industry didn't take a hit? Manufacturing was the fastest sector in the entire economy to come back swinging hard. What will make an economy better? Money. What adds money to the economy? Manufacturing. It's the only industry in the entire world that adds money to the economy. Manufacturing jobs are high paying, highly skilled jobs.

What is the personal return on investment you get from leading your business? How does it nourish your soul?

I see my sketches come to life. And I start these unrealistic, most unattainable goals out there, and then I hit them. What's the next crazy thing I will do? I doubled sales in my business in less than two years. My accountant and everybody said, "Stop. A five-year goal would be nice." I had a two-year goal and did it in eighteen months.

I like setting these crazy goals and then hitting them. I'm always looking forward to the next project. I work and get paid to do what I like doing. I invent and create things, and I talk to major people around the world and give them my opinion. I have an audience of people who listen to me. Technology: it's a lot of fun.

Why do you care about getting more women involved in manufacturing?

Because all of us use the same products every day: cars, housing, all kinds of stuff. So, when you don't have a variety of input on how a designer can make something, not everyone will benefit.

One of the car companies did a foot-kick on the back of a minivan: you tap the bumper and then the door will open. The idea came from a woman because she's holding bags of groceries in her arms and can't open the door. You discover different perspectives.

And I think women pay more attention to detail. It's up to the supervisor or the boss to use people's talents. You need a pool of people to select ideas to create the ultimate product.

What haven't we talked about that you want people to know?

This question gets me excited! College isn't for everybody. I can prove to you why the person I take at my company will outperform the person who went to college in income in five years, and then, twenty years down the line: A kid goes to college for five years, the cost is $30,000 a year. They end up $150,000 in debt with no job. An eighteen-year-old person who comes to my business, works five years and gets to go to school at night. They accumulate 10,000 hours [in work and school time] and now they're a journey-person (*a higher job position which means an increase in pay*).

Say on average a person earns $30,000 a year. At the five-year mark, they're $150,000 ahead. They have a 401(k)-retirement plan, healthcare benefits, and a vacation package. The person I trained is worth ten times more than the person who comes out of college with zero experience. Twenty years down the line, a person will still be financially ahead of the college graduate. The income differential . . . I don't believe people know about this. When you work out the math, it's incredible.

CAREER ACTIVITIES

What products do you use that make you think of ways to improve them? Sketch or write out these ideas on paper.

Have you ever thought about becoming an engineer—a person who designs, builds, or maintains things? Explore the different types of engineering careers that are available.

Does the potentially high cost of a college education and the assumed debt many students face concern you or your parents? Did you know there was another option for a viable and interesting career path, and one that offers little to no school debt for education, too? The cost of college and debt are important considerations when deciding on a career and secondary education. Think this over for yourself, and talk about it with your parents or guardians.

Explore the kinds of careers that are offered in engineering, the skilled trades, and other STEM fields.

• • •

***Precision Metal Stamping** A process of converting a flat piece of metal into various shapes by using a tool and die surface. Common metal stamping operations are piercing, bending, embossing, and progressive stamping, where multiple dies are used to make a part.

**The skills of the management team always determine whether a business will achieve long-term, sustainable success or struggle or fail during difficult economic times. Many businesses go 'out of business' during a recession because of not having enough cash to sustain operations. The reason this happens can be attributed to many different factors. In a broad sense, the most common reasons for a business failing are poor operational and financial management practices, and not keeping up with changes in customers' needs and preferences.

Debra Sommers

Title: President

Company: Lakeview Precision Machining, Inc.

Location: South Elgin, Illinois

Manufacturing Processes: CNC Precision Machining and Swiss Turning*

Industries Served: Construction, Off-Road Vehicles, Medical Equipment, Firearm / Accessories, Gun Cleaning Equipment for the Sport Industry and the Military, Office Furniture and Equipment, and Food

Examples of Products Made: Components for metering and controlling the flow of liquids, gun-cleaning equipment, assemblies (a distinct piece / part consisting of a combination of pieces / parts) used in off-road vehicles that may include springs, washers, nuts, and studs

Number of Employees: 19

Personal Interests: Faith, family, and reading the Bible and leadership and business books

• • •

Faith, Family, Integrity

You can learn a lot about a person just by observing their personal space. The handcrafted pictures and phrases ornamenting the walls caught my attention as I entered the lobby of Lakeview Precision Machining, Inc. While I waited to meet with Debra "Debbie" Sommers, I studied these holiday season decorations more closely. They made the room feel festive and "homey."

On one wall, a green, wood-tiled Christmas tree was adorned with handmade decorations. Behind the desk the wall was festooned with photographs of people in a shop setting, standing with a smiling blonde-haired woman who I recognized as Debbie. I also noticed a photograph that was decades old. It was sepia-toned, and the couple sported clothing and hairstyles from another time. I wondered who they might be.

I found that I felt very comfortable in this room. My impression was that whoever had hung the decorations and pictures was a person who cared about family and people. I soon found that Debbie was indeed someone who I felt comfortable around, and someone who seemed to really care about people and her family. As she walked toward me, a large, warm smile spread across her face and an air of peace and calm emanated from her.

Debbie became president of Lakeview Precision Machining, Inc. in February 2007. She has worked there for over three decades and is a quintessential example to others that there are opportunities for career advancement and growth for women in the manufacturing industry. The company is proof-positive that manufacturing is not only a man's domain: Debbie's two daughters, her daughter-in-law, her sister, and a number of other women work devotedly by her side in the business.

She started as a receptionist at Lakeview in 1980, and her career progressed from there. She was put in charge of accounting, then handled production responsibilities, and then she rose to the position of general manager. Then, in early 2007, she bought the company from the owner.

You may know that women-owned manufacturing companies are rare. You may also not be surprised to learn that less than 18 percent of owners of manufacturing businesses have an "exit strategy" or successors in place to lead the business when they retire. But did you know that this lack of successors presents an opportunity for both women and men to move through and up the ranks of a company and be a viable successor to a business owner—someone who has the foresight to plan for this possible scenario—when there are no successors in place or family members who are "ready and able" to run the business when the owner retires.

Debbie was in the right place, at the right time, but also, her golden opportunity to buy and run her own business was hard earned.

Lakeview doesn't blink an eye about hiring women to work on the production floor. The male employees have always accepted the women at the company—no doubt because of the existence of the strong, respectful leadership at the top.

Debbie feels that if more women looked at manufacturing they would see the boundless opportunities it offers. With almost half of Lakeview Precision's employees being women, she knows firsthand that women can do it.

She has created a family culture at Lakeview. She cares deeply for her employees and customers, and she cultivates strong relationships by delivering what she promises. To her, everybody matters. Debbie openly says that her faith is the bedrock of her life. She says it provides her with a foundation of strength, and that she uses its guiding principles in all of her relationships, both personal and professional. She says it helps her lead her employees with integrity to a prosperous future and lasting legacy.

• • •

How many years have you been active in the business?

Thirty-seven years. I started in February 1980 as a receptionist. I got the job by answering an ad in the newspaper out of high school. It's been a great career for me. When people say that there's a stigma attached to it [women working in manufacturing], we can get past that without a doubt: I think if you get someone in the door, on the plant floor, they'll see what it's like.

Do you have daughters that work in the business?

Yes. Emily, my oldest, and Cassandra, my second-oldest daughter. My youngest daughter, Kaylee, comes in once in a while. She's still going to school and is busy doing that.

How many years has Lakeview Precision Machining, Inc. been in business?

The company started in 1950 in Lakeview, Chicago. Then moved to Elgin in the '70s.

The company does CNC-precision machining?

All turning. We take [metal] bar stock and do different operations to turn it into parts. We started out strictly as a screw machine house (*in which small-to medium-sized automated machines are used*), and now we have Swiss turning centers (*which make more complicated parts and hold tighter tolerances than screw machines*).

How did you get to where you are now leading your company?

I started out as a receptionist. Then there were issues with a woman in the office who became ill. So, I was taught other aspects of the business—mostly the accounting part. I was going to school for accounting, so this fit perfectly.

Then I moved from accounting into office management, then into production—in the shop, scheduling, doing things like that. I was working directly under the owner. The more he saw that I liked the business, the more trust he put in me and the more he taught me.

Did he have a successor? Do you think he saw you as a potential successor?

I don't know if he even thought about it. He had kids. They got their educations in various fields. Some came back to work here. But it wasn't a good fit for them. They were just coming back to run dad's business. It wasn't necessarily something they aspired to do.

The more I worked out in the shop with the guys, the more the guys taught me, too. Later, the owner started taking a lot of time off work. He and his wife had a place in Wisconsin. He would only come down to his shop a couple times a month.

Were you managing the business?

Yes. When he was away, he'd phone into the office. We'd fax the figures and the numbers to him and communicate that way. He always kept his foot in the business. But he let me run the day-to-day operations. That's when I began learning more about the shop floor and the logistics part of the business. I had to do purchasing and learned the business from the ground up.

Did you consider the owner of the business a mentor?

Absolutely I would consider him a mentor. I think people, in general, are my mentors. I love people, and to listen to their stories. I love to hear where they've been, learn from their mistakes, and learn from their successes. We can learn from other people.

So, I followed him because he was my boss. I mean, he knew where everything was. He knew how to do everything he was teaching me. But you must be teachable. You must be able to learn and listen to people, take advice, and take criticism. A thirty-some-year-old male employee at the company . . . he taught me a lot, too. He would be another mentor.

Then we started hiring women.

When did the company start hiring women? When you became the president? Or was it before that?

It was before I became president. We started by hiring some women to run the machines. The owner was like, "Wow. These women are really good." And I'm like, "I know, aren't they?"

What led to more women being hired?

There was a shortage of men applying for jobs. Some of our employees would bring their wives or their daughters in to try to get a job. We came to find out that it wasn't just that we were helping them find employment. They were helping us. The women were the fastest on some machines. It was amazing how fast their hands could work, how diligent they were, and they stayed at it all day. One of the first women we hired, nobody could compete with her. Then we hired a couple more women.

The owner was so impressed by them, and he was like, "Yeah, this is really good. Let's do this."

Were the men on the shop floor accepting of the women working there?

They accepted the women. It's because we introduced them as being an asset and not as competition. There was a need we had to fill. If we had brought the women in and said, "They're here to take your place or to take your job," that would not have gone well. But they [the men] saw the need. We brought the women in and the men accepted them. They respected them for what they could do. I think respect comes from management and ownership. You've got to show respect at the top.

Do you believe manufacturing is a good career choice for women?

Absolutely. Manufacturing is a good career choice for anybody who likes to see how things work, why things work, or just likes to be creative.

I look at manufacturing as an art. People make things. You're designing ways to make things. If you haven't designed them, then you're figuring out the best way to make things. So, I think this is a great fit for anyone, especially women, because we bring something different to the table. We are made differently, we think differently.

With more women in the workforce supporting their families, this is a great place to work. I believe if more women would just give it a chance and come in and see what we're doing, see what we have to offer, see the pay scale . . . You can work in the front office all the way out to engineering and the shop floor. There are no limitations for women in this industry. Male or female, we're shorthanded. We need help.

There are men, who don't want the women they love working in a manufacturing environment, who say, "I love my wife, my sister, my girlfriend too much to put them in that environment." It's not that environment anymore. It's not smoke-filled and grease-on-the-floor. Do we get our hands dirty? Yeah, we do. But it's a fun dirty with the stuff we're doing.

What types of jobs are available in your manufacturing company?

We could use a woman to set-up the machines. We could use a woman to program the machines. We could use a woman to stock (*load material into*) the machines. We could use a woman to change the tools and check the pieces (*to make sure they meet quality specifications*). We could use someone in the shipping and receiving department. We could use someone washing parts. Those are areas where we are continually ready to promote one person and bring in the next person if they were available.

Is there a career path for people in this company?

Absolutely. Our plant manager started out in our secondary department twenty-five years ago operating a machine. He's now our plant manager and number-one guy on the shop floor. If he were a woman, it would be the same thing. We could start her off operating a machine, learning how to make intricate parts, and from there, grow up to be the plant manager. There's no reason she couldn't do it.

Do you offer employee training?

We train internally. One guy on the shop floor that is programming our CNCs (*Computer Numerical Control machines*), we hired as a temp.

We trained him. There's training available all around. What we don't train for in-house, we send people out for training.

What do you believe are the three biggest misconceptions women have about working in/having a career in manufacturing?

It's dirty and not a place for women. It's a man's job.

I think many women think men don't want them to be part of it. I haven't seen that to be true very often. The few times I have experienced that I chose to ignore it.

Women have heard people say this isn't a place for them. That's not the case. More than 90 percent of people welcome women—welcome people that want to learn, male or female.

Women are not excluded from this industry. The mindset they must have is: "I'm not going to be left out because I'm female."

We both got our start in manufacturing in the '80s and '90s when there weren't many women involved. Do you think things have changed?

Absolutely. Years ago, when I would go to a meeting, I would be one of the few women at this all-male function, and it made me feel like an outsider. But it's how you perceive yourself, you know, and how you present yourself. If you go in there thinking you're an outsider and that you're inferior, then you're going to be. But if you go in there saying, "I'm here for the same reason you're here. I'm an equal. Accept me or move over." I think how you get accepted is all about your own perception. How you think about yourself as you're going in? How you present yourself? Show up? "Move over and let me sit next to you. I'll keep up with you. If I don't keep up with you, then I'll ask you a question. If there are some things you can't keep up with me about, then you can ask me questions."

What advancements do you see happening in manufacturing over the next five years that will create opportunities for people who are considering a career in manufacturing?

I hear people talk about robotics and how they will replace people. Well, yes, robotics will replace some people. But we need people to design the robots. To build the robots. To come up with ideas to improve the robots. To service the robots. If you think about it, robotics will increase the workforce because we're adding capacity.

What resources would you recommend to young women (or even their parents) who are considering a career in manufacturing to help them learn more?

I would say go to your high school counselors and tell them you're interested. I think we're finding some high schools are finally getting onboard. But some high schools still don't get it.

I would encourage students to go to their community colleges and talk to them. Go to the International Machine Tool Show or the Technology and Manufacturing Association or the Precision Machined Products Association. Call anyone involved in manufacturing. Manufacturers welcome people to come to visit their plants. Look, spend a day with someone: a manager, an owner, or someone else. Hang out with them for a day and see what they do. See how challenging it is. See how rewarding it is. Employees enjoy coming to work. And at the end of the day, they can see what they made.

To explore manufacturing as a career, reach out to manufacturers in your community. Say, "I'm not positive what I want to do. I want to know what your business is about. It interests me. It intrigues me. I want to learn." This is a good place to start. The manufacturing industry is rewarding and diverse with what you can do.

What books are you reading right now?

I read the Bible every day. That is my firm foundation. I get most everything from God's word. I really put my faith in that.

I'm also reading *Traction: Get a Grip on Your Business* (by Gino Wickman), and *Boundaries for Leaders* (by Dr. Henry Cloud) is another one. I want to find a good fiction book because I've read so many leadership and business books, I think it's time to read something for fun.

What's your number one piece of advice to young women (and their parents) who are considering a career in manufacturing?

Investigate. Ask questions. Don't think there is anything you are not capable of getting involved in or doing. If you have a desire for something, don't hesitate just because you're female. Don't think the doors are closed because you're female because that is not what happens.

Don't think because a woman tries to get involved in a man's world, she is anything less than an associate or an equal.

There are women in the industry who own a business and their offices are pink and smell really good. That's fine if that's what you want. You can't even smell the shop floor. But if you don't mind going home and smelling like cutting oil, you'll like it here. I really like that smell!

What is the personal return on investment you get from leading your business? How does it nourish your soul?

To know I come to work, and there are nineteen people here, and what I do impacts their livelihoods. This fuels me every day. If I come to work and I don't feel like doing what I'm doing today, I think about the people who are counting on me to come to work and make things happen. And they're coming to work, and they are just as valuable as I am. They're coming to work for this whole team. It is rewarding to know I can impact these people's lives by coming to work every day, showing up, and doing the best I possibly can.

Why do you care about getting more women involved in manufacturing?

Because they're an untapped resource. We need more creative people involved in the industry. I heard today that manufacturing only employs 10 percent of the workforce. We could be so much bigger and better in the United States if we would tap into women. Let's get them onboard for manufacturing because I know they would do well. I know they can do it.

What haven't we talked about that you want people to know?

That when you're a business owner or a manager, people think you need to put in ten, twelve hours a day to be successful. That's unnecessary. You must have people around you to make you successful. You have to put faith and trust in the people around you. So, build your team up around you so you can help them, bring them right along with you. Don't feel you have to be the Lone Ranger, because you're not.

If you look around at how many women work here, [you can see that] we welcome them with open arms. We welcome everybody with open arms. But I think women migrate here because they think we will allow them to succeed as much as they can. Because of my belief in God, I never want to offend people. But I hope to have an eternal impact on people by how I do business.

CAREER ACTIVITIES

What do you think about Debbie starting as a receptionist, then buying the company from the owner and becoming the president of the company? Can you imagine yourself doing this someday?

What part of Debbie's story did you find most interesting and why?

Have you thought about touring manufacturing plants that are owned by women? Look for some in your area and ask if you can see what manufacturing is all about.

What books or other resources do you read, watch, or listen to, or things do you practice that give you inspiration and strength to overcome the obstacles in your way? Find a way to incorporate those good tools into your life each day.

• • •

***CNC (Computer Numerical Control) Precision Machining** A process used in manufacturing that involves the use of computers to control machinery that makes complicated patterns and shapes in a highly automated way, and with a high degree of repeatable accuracy.

Swiss Turning A specialized process performed on a Swiss-style lathe for machining small, high-precision turned parts, such as medical components.

A Swiss machine deflects and vibrates less than a traditional CNC lathe because of the use of a guide bushing, a holding mechanism that is placed in front of the collet. The purpose of a guide bushing is to offer additional support to stock material when the part is being machined or turned.

The Women of Lakeview Precision Machining, Inc.

Company: Lakeview Precision Machining, Inc.

Location: South Elgin, Illinois

Manufacturing Processes: CNC Precision Machining and Swiss Turning*

Industries Served: Construction, Off-Road Vehicles, Medical Equipment, Firearm/Accessories, Gun Cleaning Equipment for the Sport Industry and the Military, Office Furniture and Equipment, and Food

Examples of Products Made: Components for metering and controlling the flow of liquids, gun-cleaning equipment, assemblies (a distinct piece/part consisting of a combination of pieces/parts) used in off-road vehicles that may include springs, washers, nuts, and studs

Number of Employees: 19

The Women:

Emily Mitchell, Human Resources, Accounting, Order Entry

Cassie Sommers, Scheduling and Material

Stephanie Suerth, Quality Inspector

MaryJo Lanz, Purchasing

Kim Beal, Administrative Assistant

Tonya Reyes, Machine Operator

• • •

A Family Affair

Lakeview Precision Machining, Inc. is, without question, a woman-owned, women-operated, family-oriented business. Nearly half of their employees are women. It was interesting to hear many perspectives from these women about what it's like to work in manufacturing.

Debbie Sommers, Lakeview's president, considers herself fortunate to be able to work beside her daughters: Emily, Cassie, and Stephanie; her sister, Kim; and the many other women working at the company.

Some women work in the office performing administrative and purchasing activities. Others work in the plant on the shop floor—in quality control or in the shipping and receiving departments. It delighted me to receive a broad-sweeping perspective of how these women feel about their jobs in the manufacturing industry. All of them concurred that manufacturing is an excellent place for women to be. There is room for everybody.

Debbie and the women of Lakeview Precision Machining welcome women with wide, open arms.

• • •

How did you get to where you are now working at Lakeview Precision Machining, Inc.?

MaryJo: I went to Penn State University and was a business logistics major. When I graduated, I worked for Westinghouse Electric. We were a private contractor for the naval nuclear program, and I was in purchasing there. After I had my first child, I stayed home for nineteen years. I met Debbie [Sommers] through my oldest child—our daughters played volleyball together. Debbie needed help in purchasing, so I came back [to work] part-time.

Stephanie: I worked in retail. The company shut down, closed. So then I became a stay-at-home mom for two years. Then my dad gave me an opportunity, and I operated, set up, and programmed Swiss machines for five years. Then I got laid off and my dad said they [Lakeview Precision Machining, Inc.] needed [quality] inspectors, so I came here.

Group chatter:

She's the best quality inspector we've ever had.

She's really good!

She stands up to the guys. They say, "It's okay." But she says, "No. No, it isn't."

She stands up for herself.

She doesn't let up.

Emily: I worked for Lakeview back when we were in Elgin; I filed things. When the company moved I had just graduated from high school, and I was unsure what path I wanted. So, I started at ECC (*Elgin*

Community College), where I met my husband, and I would work here part-time. Between then and now, I left working for the company] a lot. I worked a lot of retail, at a retirement center serving food . . . I had a bunch of odd jobs. But I always ended up coming back here.

After community college, I went to NIU (*Northern Illinois University*) and got my bachelor's degree in speech-language pathology. I completed my bachelor's, then found out how expensive a master's degree was. I put that off. I really dove into working here at that point, and that was four years ago.

But I kept telling myself that I would not stay here, and would not work for my mom for the rest of my life, and that there were better things out there. A couple years ago, I took a teaching job. I taught preschool for three years, and I again ended up coming back here. Now that I've set aside the idea I had in my head of what it was to work for your mom, I love what I do. My role in the company is growing, which I really enjoy. I don't feel that stigma of "working for your mom" anymore. Now I think, "How can I grow the company to how my mom wants it to be, and eventually, what Cassie (*Emily's sister*) and I want it to be?" After getting over my "problem" of working for the family, it's been a fun experience. I'm looking forward to where it's going next.

Cassie: I have been in and out [of the family business] since I was in high school, though not as much as Emily. I've always had a desire to be here. But when I first went to college, I went for marine biology, but my head was not there, so I totally failed out.

Then I went to ECC (*Elgin Community* College) and started taking business classes. I enjoyed it, but I didn't finish.

Then I was working here. Mom fired me because she wanted me to get other experiences. So, I did serving jobs. After I did that for a couple years, I came back here, and she gave me a job because they fired the shipping and receiving guy. She had me do that. I've been doing shipping and receiving for almost three years. I'm now in scheduling and going back to school to get a couple certificates in supply-chain management.

Kim: Debbie offered me work at Lakeview to get me out of the house because I felt cooped-up:

I was working [only] out of my home at the time. I started part-time. Before I knew it, I had been at the company for five years.

When Debbie bought the company, at that point, I had to take time off for medical reasons. Six months later, I came back. Then Debbie started the business here [in South Elgin]. I'm still here.

I want to learn more things. I've seen Debbie grow. She got thrown into this without schooling or anything. She had to figure it out herself. It is amazing what she's done.

Do you believe manufacturing is a good career choice for women?

Emily: I used to not think it was. I used to have the same stigma in my head I think a lot of other people have: it's an old man's career, young people don't have any place here, women don't have a place here because it's all men in the shop. But my view on that has changed since working here. Seeing people like Stephanie and Cassie running machines and doing everything else that the guys are doing.

People used to think it was such a dark and dirty and scary place to work. But the factories now are high-class, well-performing shops. This changed my mind, so I think women have many places in manufacturing, and not just in the office, but also on the production line.

Cassie: Stephanie runs the machines. She'll do the [material] reloads. When the guys are not here, she'll run the machines. I've only done a couple things on the machines, like working on the secondary machines (*machines that do minor machining or finishing of parts*). I'm out in Shipping.

You don't really know what it's like [working in manufacturing] until you live it. After getting back into shipping and receiving, I want to stay back there. I check on the material. That's the little part I do out in the shop.

Emily: It's important to have women in the shop. Women create a connection between the guys in the shop and the office. They bring those relationships into the office. It's not "us" versus "them." It opens up communication.

Cassie: We have a great team of guys, and they're so smart, and it's awesome to see everybody's qualities integrate. Women bring organization into the shop with the guys.

Emily: We used to have guys afraid to talk to us in the office. Now they come in and out and they have coffee and conversations with us.

Stephanie: I never thought that because I'm a woman I can't work in a man's job. I don't see the "women's struggle." I have gone on interviews and been told, "It's a male-based industry." For me, it's not an issue. But I know for other people it is.

Emily: For my sisters and I, having our mom who's running everything—it really changes things: we don't even see that anymore (*that it's significant that a woman is in charge and that that woman is their mom*); it's not something that crosses our minds anymore. The whole family thing is great. It can be a challenge. But it's great. Who gets to work with five of their family members, including their mother and two sisters?

What do you believe are the three biggest misconceptions women have about working in/having a career in manufacturing?

Emily: You have to be strong.

Stephanie: Must have physical abilities.

Cassie: When I went to high school, nobody said anything about manufacturing. So when you go to college, you don't take any classes in manufacturing because you know nothing about it. But now there are different things being done to get the word about manufacturing spread to the high schools.

Emily: If we didn't have a mom in manufacturing, we wouldn't know anything about it. Until we went to TMA (*Technology and Manufacturing Association*) and PMPA (*Precision Machined Products Association*) meetings, I was unaware of how many women are involved in manufacturing. You go to a meeting [now/one of these meetings], and there are hundreds of women there. This is a much larger force than I realized.

Why is manufacturing a good career choice for women?

Cassie: It's fun. You're always learning something new, and there are always ways to improve yourself.

Emily: It's an intellectually challenging workplace; [you're] solving problems.

Stephanie: You see things and wonder, "How could I make that?" Then see what you can make.

MaryJo: Just do it because it's what you want to do, and it's what you are passionate about.

Cassie: Train people up from high school. Work to find inspiration. My inspiration came from working in the shop. Now I'm going to school. I pay attention so much more because I know what I'm learning can be applied at work right away. If you know you want to go to school for manufacturing, then do it.

Why do you care about getting more women involved in manufacturing?

Stephanie: To get women involved in every aspect of every industry.

Cassie: Any industry can benefit from having women.

Emily: Women have a lot to bring to the table.

Tonya: Just so women know it's not a "woman versus man" thing, women need to have the confidence they can do it. It still is a male-dominated industry. Don't think: "You shouldn't even try because men won't accept you." Take away that fear. It does not matter that you are a woman; know what you bring to the table.

What haven't we talked about that you want people to know?

Emily: I think it's important to take the "men versus women" stigma out. You are a human being that can do these jobs which makes you viable in any industry . . .

Cassie: . . . whether you are a man or a woman.

Emily: As long as you've got the work ethic and a desire to learn more . . .

Cassie: . . . and a desire to grow.

CAREER ACTIVITIES

How many different jobs do the women interviewed in this story have? Which ones interest you? Which ones do you want to learn more about?

Did Emily resist working at Lakeview? What were her reasons? What changed her mind, and what does she believe about manufacturing and women in manufacturing now?

How do you think you would feel working in a manufacturing plant with other women? What do you think it would be like?

• • •

***CNC (Computer Numerical Control) Precision Machining** A process used in manufacturing that involves the use of computers to control machinery that makes complicated patterns and shapes in a highly automated way, and with a high degree of repeatable accuracy.

Swiss Turning A specialized process performed on a Swiss-style lathe for machining small, high-precision turned parts, such as medical components. A Swiss machine deflects and vibrates less than a traditional CNC lathe because of the use of a guide bushing, a holding mechanism that is placed in front of the collet. The purpose of a guide busing is to offer additional support to stock material when the part is being machined or turned.

Renee Schroeder

Title: Vice President of Operations

Company: Smith & Richardson, Inc.

Location: Geneva, Illinois

Manufacturing Processes: CNC Precision Machining, Precision Metal Stamping, Precision Slide-Forming*

Industries Served: Aerospace, Medical, Casting, Sports/Recreation, Transportation, and other various industries

Examples of Products Made: Components for force and vibration sensors that are used on aircraft to measure braking torque and force, and in-flight controls; components in meters that help measure the flow of liquids and gases; triggers on cross bows and other pieces for the sports industry.

Number of Employees: 51

Personal Interests: Reading books

• • •

The Door is Open

Renee Schroeder has a quiet disposition. But don't be fooled. Right beneath her calm demeanor, there's a powerful undercurrent of discipline, and a drive for accountability and getting things done.

Like so many women, Renee didn't plan on having a career in manufacturing. It was just happenstance that after graduating from college with an accounting degree, she landed her first job at Smith &

Richardson, Inc., taking on the tasks of handling the bookkeeping, accounting, and IT (Information Technology).

IT was just emerging in manufacturing, and as the youngest employee, she was "a natural" to take on this charge. From that initial position, her responsibilities grew over the years to encompass everything from expediting orders for customers, to purchasing materials and supplies, to doing human resource activities. Her employer, Rich Hoster, the president of Smith & Richardson, told me Renee has a handle on the "pulse of everything going on in the plant," and she is now the vice president of operations.

As we chatted, Renee shared with me that in high school, guidance counselors never presented the skilled trades to her as a career option. We discussed our similar experiences about how most high school students get channeled into college prep.

Guidance counselors often only present the skilled trades as a career based on what they *think* is a student's potential, or as is often the case with the trades, a *lack* of career potential. This is old economy and social thinking because manufacturing today differs greatly from what it was like fifty years ago. And it has drastically changed from what it was like one hundred years ago, which, unfortunately, is still the image many people have about the field.

Because of rapid advancements in technology, much of manufacturing today operates with technical, state-of-the-art equipment. That equipment, along with today's laws, requires operations to take place in a clean and safe work environment; manufacturing is forward-looking. It must be to remain competitive in the global marketplace. There are many career opportunities and, as of this writing, the pay has never been better.

Renee has been introducing her three daughters to the world of manufacturing. Sometimes they go to work with her. They understand what is being made, and how that is being accomplished using sophisticated machinery. She said that she would never have considered a career in manufacturing had she not taken that first job at Smith & Richardson, and she wants her daughters to be more aware than she was about the many different types of careers that are available.

Renee wants to get the message out to young women to take a closer look at manufacturing as a career choice. She knows from firsthand experience that it offers an open door that can lead to great career opportunities for young women. She should know because she's a model for what a successful career path (bookkeeper / accountant to vice president of operations) in manufacturing looks like.

• • •

How many years have you worked at Smith & Richardson?

I have been here fourteen years.

What was your position when you started?

Accounting and IT. I'm still doing that, and have taken on more responsibilities as I've gotten into it.

Your job title is vice president of operations. What is your background? Before you took this position, what experience did you have?

Working here was my first main job out of college. I went to school for accounting, and I didn't grow up in manufacturing at all. My grandpa did, and my uncles were in manufacturing, but as far as my parents, they were not. So, this was a whole new thing. I knew nothing about manufacturing when I started here. I like manufacturing now that I've been in it, and I wouldn't want to leave it.

What do you like about it?

I think it's just that it means something in the sense that you're building stuff and it's going somewhere else, so there's a purpose to it.

What industries does your company serve?

We serve a variety of industries. There's aerospace, medical, agriculture. Let's see . . . gas and oil, gaming—which would be like crossbows and gun parts—pumps . . . There are a bunch of different industries we focus on.

Can you tell me more about your journey from being an accountant/bookkeeper to becoming vice president of operations?

I just kind of got more involved. I was focusing on the customers and dealing more with the customers. I got more knowledge of everything that's on the shop floor. I gained lots of perspective about how everything's made and the processes we go through to get parts made.

I was checking on the delivery status of customers' orders and found out where they were at in the [manufacturing] process. I've gotten to know a lot of the processes (*of how products are made*) and how everything goes. It's amazing how much I've learned. When I think back to when I started working here, I knew nothing. Realizing everything I know now, it's hard to describe how I've learned it all.

Do you get involved in any other activities, such as quality control, purchasing, or even employee training?

That all falls under me now. As things would change, things would fall onto my plate. So, then I'd learn it through that way.

I ended up doing purchasing. That's under me, too. IT was just accidental because I was one of the younger people that started here. That's how I ended up doing IT. Then the purchasing and accounting stuff, I fell into all of it.

Do you still work in accounting?

Yes. I do HR (*Human Resources*) too. We used to have a HR person. But then, as we shrunk (*the number of employees*), we didn't need someone in HR full time. We're not at that cusp where we need an actual full-time HR person, so that falls under me, too. That's why he [Rich Hoster] says I do everything. I know everything that's going on.

Did you have any mentors along the path of your career?

I've learned everything from Rich. He's taught me a lot. That's how I've gotten to what I know today. I've learned a lot from him and how he does things. Even though he and I are completely different [in personality], I've learned things that he does and can incorporate them into my own style.

Do you believe manufacturing is a good career choice for women?

I definitely do. I have three girls myself, and I've told my husband about this. Before I worked here, I wouldn't have known that (*manufacturing is a good career choice for women*). But since working here, I can see all the opportunities and different paths that you can take in manufacturing. It's not just working on the shop floor. There are other opportunities. We need manufacturing because there will always be things [components] that need to go into other things [finished products]. It amazes me the things that we've made that go into little parts that you wouldn't even think you would need.

What jobs are available in manufacturing at Smith & Richardson for people who want to get into manufacturing?

There are always the office positions: there's customer service, purchasing, and QC (*quality control*). In QC there's a lot of measurement and it is detail-oriented—many people forget about that one, even though it's one of the most important aspects of manufacturing. You want to provide a quality part, and we make sure that it's good before it goes out to the customer. So that's always a good one. Working on the machines, shipping/receiving, etc.

Do you have any engineers on staff?

Yes. We have mechanical engineers that do all of our programming for the machines. We redraw all of our customers' prints, so they all have the same format in the shop. We use our engineers for doing that. And technical questions, like when a person has a hard time setting up the machine or needs feedback. Stuff like that. Engineers are a crucial part of our company.

What do you believe are the three biggest misconceptions women have about a career/careers in manufacturing?

That it's male-dominated. That it's dirty. And there's no career path.

In response, what do you say?

It's a clean environment. It's technical. It's advanced compared to what it used to be back a long time ago.

What advanced technologies do you use in this business?

We use computers heavily (*on the manufacturing floor and in the day-to-day operations and management of the business*). All of our customers' orders come through email. We rarely get phone calls anymore. We get a few faxes or EDIs (*Electronic Data Interchange*) between their systems to our computer system. Even when we ship, everything gets processed through the computer. All (*machining and manufacturing*) programs get sent to the controls of the machines to make the parts.

What advancements do you see happening in manufacturing over the next five years that will create opportunities for people who are considering a career in manufacturing?

More technology. So even with robots, you still need someone that knows how to run the robots. Robots will not replace all people. They will help make you more efficient. You will always need people that can run the machines and program them.

What resources would you recommend to young women (or even their parents) who are considering a career in manufacturing to help them learn more?

Talk to people in the community, especially those in the manufacturing businesses. That's what we do here. We try to open our doors to any high school student, or younger child, that wants to learn more about manufacturing to see what it is all about. We encourage the parents to come along with their kids.

Because parents have a huge influence, don't they?

Yes. One of my daughters comes here with me sometimes. It's funny. The other day when she brought a friend with her, and as we were leaving, she was telling her friend all about the things that we do. It was kind of neat hearing her—she's only nine—trying to explain, "Oh, that's where they do their shipping," and "They make parts there," and stuff like that.

I'm sure a lot of girls that age, like your daughter's friend, have never been to a place like this before, correct?

Yes. It really opened her eyes. Reaching young women, I think it is so important. It was nice hearing that she likes what I'm doing. She'll understand what manufacturing is before she chooses a career.

We've even talked about, maybe during the summer, trying to get middle school students to come in for manufacturing boot camp, so they can get a more hands-on feeling for what manufacturing is all about.

I've learned a lot from being here and seeing what manufacturing is. It's helped me in raising my kids to know that there are other career options out there. When I went to school it [the message] was "go to college." That's something you were supposed to do. So, knowing that there are other options. This definitely opened my eyes to that.

Was your experience in high school the same as mine: that the skilled trades were not talked about much?

Right. I wish that they would have maybe told us more about it in high school—to see more options. Give everyone the opportunity to learn about the trades. Not just the people that might show an interest.

Why do you think manufacturing is a good career choice for a young woman?

I think there are many opportunities. There is more opportunity than people realize. Even though we work with metal, other manufacturers work with paper, chemicals, and other materials. There are endless opportunities in different companies.

I didn't know what manufacturing was when I went to school. You hear about agriculture and you hear about some trade stuff, but never about actual manufacturing and what it was. When I came to Smith & Richardson I was as green as they come.

What's your number one piece of advice to young women (and their parents) who are considering a career in manufacturing?

How about if you try it? You never know unless you try something whether you will like it. Be open-minded because you might not know something's out there. Once you see it you think, "Wow, this really was for me."

What is the personal return on investment you get from this business? How does it nourish your soul?

It feels like I'm doing something. I'm making something, and it will be used to make something else. I feel like there's an end purpose to it. Even though I might not know what the end use of the part is, I know it's going somewhere and doing something important. I like knowing that what I'm doing has a purpose.

Why do you care about getting more women involved in manufacturing?

Because when I first started I was one of a few women in the trade associations. It's nice to have other women . . . and the conversations can be different when it's all males versus having women in there. Today there are more opportunities for women. It's not just a male-dominated industry. There are opportunities for women too.

Do you feel that the industry is open to more women coming into it?

I think they have been. I definitely have seen a change over the years compared to when I first went to the trade association meetings to now. There are definitely more women now than there ever has been. So that's nice to see. I think they've been open to it. I don't think they have ever opposed them. They never treated women in a different way or anything. I think women just weren't there.

What haven't we talked about that you want people to know?

We've covered a lot . . . just that manufacturing is a good career, and there are lots of opportunities. And it's not just for males. There are many opportunities for women, too.

CAREER ACTIVITIES

What are all the different job responsibilities Renee has had at Smith & Richardson? Which ones interest you the most?

Did you hear about working in the skilled trades or manufacturing at school or somewhere else? What were you told? Was it explained that it can be an exciting career or not?

Why does Renee feel that working in manufacturing is a good career choice for women?

After reading Renee's story, does a career in manufacturing seem more exciting? If so, in what way?

• • •

***CNC (Computer Numerical Control) Precision Machining** A process used in manufacturing that involves the use of computers to control machinery that makes complicated patterns and shapes in a highly automated way, and with a high degree of repeatable accuracy.

Precision Metal Stamping A process of converting a flat piece of metal into various shapes by using a tool and die surface. Common metal stamping operations are piercing, bending, embossing, and progressive stamping, where multiple dies are used to make a part.

Precision Slide-Forming A metal stamping process that combines the progressive die process, which consists of several individual workstations, each of which performs one or more different operations on the part. The ability to produce components in this way allows for the possibility of performing multiple cutting and/or forming operations simultaneously.

Closing Thoughts

As the idea for this book crystallized in my mind, I was confident I needed to tell the stories of women who were some of the trailblazers in manufacturing, who got their start in the 70s, 80s, and before, when women in manufacturing were an anomaly, and give them the recognition they deserve for clearing the road. These women set the stage for the young women leading and working in manufacturing today.

It is with vital energy that we, the "seasoned generation," pass on the baton to the younger generation, continue to do our part to advance manufacturing as a viable career choice and a path to economic empowerment for women, and end the stigma around women working in manufacturing.

When I asked all of the women I interviewed for the book what advice they would offer to young women (and their parents) who are contemplating a career in manufacturing, what I repeatedly heard was that students are rarely told about the skilled trades or manufacturing as a possible career choice. If someone does mention it, they do it hastily to move onto something else that is perceived to be a more desirable career choice. They do not do this in malice; it is done because many people aren't familiar with the manufacturing industry.

It is up to us who do know about manufacturing to show and tell others what an incredible industry it is to be part of, and why that is so. I believe that the knowledge gathered in this book will serve as a tool for greater awareness about the fantastic career opportunities in manufacturing.

Manufacturing offers a technologically innovative career that's highly relevant in the future. Manufacturing companies are looking for people who have an aptitude for science, technology, engineering, and mathematics. These skills are becoming increasingly important as manufacturing technology evolves.

Women have low participation and representation in these STEM-related jobs of the future, yet they offer good income potential and benefits. Manufacturing workers are educated professionals: over fifty percent of people in manufacturing have some level of college education, and job openings are surging because of retiring baby boomers. A career in manufacturing pays well even if a person does not have a college degree. What I also heard repeatedly from the women I interviewed is that the door is wide open, and they are encouraging you to walk through it.

Manufacturing is creating many exciting opportunities for women and men of all ages. I hope you will be inspired to explore manufacturing and other STEM fields as a potential career path. I hope you enjoyed reading this book as much as I enjoyed writing it. I will have reached my goal if it has sparked your interest to explore the manufacturing industry as a career option, and that through reading this book and the women's stories contained in it, you learned something new, or something that you didn't know before, about today's manufacturing industry. Please send your success stories to me at brichter@profit-strategies.com as you embark on your exciting career in manufacturing and enjoy its rewards. I can't wait to read them.

PART 3:
MORE TO EXPLORE

Recommended Resources

There is an abundance of resources from which to learn more about manufacturing and STEM careers. Listed below are some of my favorite books and resources to get you started on your journey of exploring the exciting world of women in manufacturing and STEM-related careers!

Books

Hidden Figures
by Margot Lee Shetterly

This book is the story of the black female mathematicians at NASA whose calculations helped fuel some of Americas greatest achievements in space.

Lewis Carroll in Numberland: His Fantastical Mathematical Logical Life
by Robin Wilson

Lewis Carroll is best known for his books, Alice's Adventures in Wonderland and Through the Looking-Glass. In addition to his works in poetry and fiction, Carroll published findings in the fields of geometry, logic, and algebra.

Ready! Set! Soar! Your Guide to Building a Career Without a College Degree
by Bobi Siembieda

It is a deeply entrenched idea in our society that you must go to college to have a successful career. This conventional wisdom is a myth. The author tells the story about her unconventional, yet successful career path. This book includes tools and resources to help build a successful career and life.

What Do You Do With an Idea?
by Kobi Yamada (Author), Mae Besom (Illustrator)

A New York Times Best Seller, this award-winning book for younger readers is excellent for anyone, of any age, who's ever had a big idea that seemed too big, odd, or difficult to entertain. This book inspired me to look at ideas, and what to do with them, differently.

Women in Science: 50 Fearless Pioneers Who Changed the World
by Rachel Ignotofsky

This book highlights the contributions of fifty notable women in the fields of science, technology, engineering, and mathematics (STEM).

Wonder Women: 25 Innovators, Inventors, and Trailblazers Who Changed History
by Sam Maggs

The author tells the stories of women who broke barriers as scientists, engineers, mathematicians, adventurers, and inventors.

Career

STEM Manufacturing Careers

Is a manufacturing or STEM-related career right for you? This website gives answers and resources to students, parents, educators, and employers. Read articles about STEM careers, other topics of interest, and much more!

https://stemjobs.com/

STEM Type™ Quiz

STEMJobs defines eight groups of manufacturing jobs and the different skills and knowledge requirements you need to succeed in each type of job. Take the quiz to find out the different types of STEM jobs that may be right for you.

https://stemjobs.com/stem-type-quiz-main/

Organizations

Center for STEM Education for Girls

The Center provides a program called the Summer Institute for girls in Grades 7 through 12, as well as research, educational materials, and other resources.

http://stemefg.org/

Manufacturing Institute

The Manufacturing Institute's aims are to change the perception of careers in manufacturing so that they align with the manufacturing industry's utilization of the most advanced, innovative technology in the U.S. The Institute is an advocate for education and job training policies that strengthen the technical skills of the U.S. manufacturing workforce. Its STEP Ahead initiative, a national program, was launched in 2012. The women in STEP Ahead have made a pledge to be leaders and promote the importance of manufacturing to women in their communities.

http://www.themanufacturinginstitute.org/

The National Institute for Women in Trades, Technology, and Science

This organization helps educators nationwide to close the gender gap for women and girls in male-dominated careers, such as technology, the trades, and law enforcement. They offer research, training, and classroom tools that help technology and science educators to increase and retain the number of women and girls that enroll in their classes.

http://www.iwitts.org/

Women In Manufacturing® (WiM)

This is a national association dedicated to supporting, promoting, and inspiring women who have chosen a career in manufacturing.

http://www.womeninmanufacturing.org/

Miscellaneous

ManufacturingStories®

Read and learn more about the revitalization and modernization of manufacturing in America.

https://manufacturingstories.com/category/manufacturing/

Women and Manufacturing Podcast | Manufacturing Talk Radio

A podcast where accomplished women in manufacturing share their experiences and encourage the next generation of women to join and follow them in this noble profession to create fulfilling lives.

https://womenandmfg.com/

Glossary

Accounting A process of recording and reporting the numerical and financial transactions from business operations over a period of time. These transactions are summarized and presented in the financial statements, including the balance sheet, income statement, and cash flow statement.

Apprentice A person who works for a company, or another person, in order to learn a trade. Apprenticeships in machining and manufacturing processes are typical examples of the types of apprenticeships in the manufacturing and engineering fields.

Automatic Turret Lathe A 1970s-era, high-precision automatic machine that runs off microswitches, mechanical relays (which control the flow of electricity), and adjustable hydraulic valve controls.

Automation A method of performing a machining process by highly automatic means through the use of electronic devices. Products are machine-made, rather than handmade, which minimizes the human intervention required to make the product.

Biotech (Biotechnology) A technology that involves the use of living organisms such as bacteria. Biotechnology is mainly used in agriculture, food science, and medicine.

Blueprint A design, pattern, or guide for making something (from a product to a building). Blueprints are traditionally made of blue paper and blue ink, but many guides or plans for making things can be called blueprints even if they are not printed on blue paper.

CAD (Computer-Aided Design) A software used by engineers, architects, drafters, artists, and others to create precision drawings or technical illustrations, two-dimensional (2-D) drawings, or three-dimensional (3-D) models.

Capital Asset Planning A model of an organizations capital expenses that provides decision-makers an effective way to justify, review, and approve new capital expenditures.

Chemical Engineer A professional who works in the chemical industry. Their main job is to convert basic raw materials into a variety of products. This person may also get involved in the design and operation of the plants and equipment that produce chemical products.

CNC (Computer Numerical Control) Precision Metal Spinning A process of turning (spinning) a flat piece of metal on a lathe around a pattern allowing the metal to form to a desired shape. Metal spinning is used when there is a need for a three-dimensional shape (e.g., hemispheres, cones) to be formed from a single piece of material (see also "Automation" and "Precision Machining").

CNC (Computer Numerical Control) Precision Machining A process used in manufacturing that involves the use of computers to control machinery that makes complicated patterns and shapes in a highly automated way, and with a high degree of repeatable accuracy (see also "Automation" and Precision Machining").

Cobalt Steel A steel made from the chemical element cobalt (Co). Cobalt is found in the earths crust. This metal is used to create magnetic, wear-resistant, and high-strength metal alloys. For example, parts that are meant to be kept in a saline (salty) or corrosive environment are often made from this steel.

Collet A metal collar that tightens around a piece of raw material or a tool, and clamps down on the object with strong force to hold it in place. Collets are often used on CNC, manual lathes, and other types of machinery.

Die A tool used in manufacturing to shape material. Dies are generally customized for the items/products they help to make. For example, in metal stamping, a surface that is customized with both tools and dies forms the metal into a desired shape.

Die Maker (or Tool and Die Maker) A class of machinists who make jigs, fixtures, dies, molds, cutting tools, gauges, and other tools used in manufacturing processes (see "Die" and "Tooling").

EDI (Electronic Data Interchange) A process to transfer data from one computer system to another without the need for human intervention. EDI permits multiple companies to exchange documents electronically.

EDM (Electrical Discharge Machining) A manufacturing process where a desired shape is obtained by using an electronically charged wire to cut materials.

Engineered Advanced Plastics A variety of plastic materials that are specifically used in innovative, high-tech applications and products. Some engineered advanced plastics are highly resistant to impact or abrasion. Others are heat resistant or have greater mechanical strength, rigidity, and chemical stability than more common plastics. Examples of engineered advanced plastics are ABS (Acrylonitrile Butadiene Styrene), Nylon 6 and 6-6, polycarbonate, Acetal, and Teflon.

Exit Strategy A business owners strategic plan to sell his or her ownership of a company to investors, employees, or another company.

Fixture A metal device that holds tooling or material sturdily in place while machining, stamping, and other types of manufacturing operations are being performed.

Human Resources (HR) A department in a company that is focused on the activities and policies that relate to employees. This departments responsibilities include the recruiting and hiring of new employees, new employee orientation (which includes explaining employee benefits, like health insurance, and the policies of the organization), the training of new and current employees, and conflict resolution, and works to help the company retain its employees.

Industrial Trades (or Industrial Skilled Trades) A classification of types of jobs that require specific training. Machinists, carpenters, tile setters, and electricians all fall into this category. Some of the labor involved in the skilled trades is manual work, which can be physically demanding.

Information Technology (IT) A technology involving the use of computer systems, software, and networks for the processing and distribution of data.

Internship A temporary position within a company where a person receives on-the-job training. An internship can be paid or unpaid.

ISO 9001 A standard quality control compliance system developed and published by the International Organization for Standardization. The best reason to follow the standard is to create an efficient quality management system.

Lathe A machine that holds and rotates a workpiece so that various machining operations such as turning, drilling, and cutting, can be performed on the workpiece. Lathes are often used with precision machining where the tools applied remove material from the workpiece in order to create the desired product.

Lean Manufacturing (or Lean Production) A systematic way to decrease waste in the manufacturing process. Its goal is to reduce cost and increase productivity and output.

Mechanical Engineering A branch of engineering that applies the principles of mechanics and materials science to analyze, design, manufacture, and maintain mechanical systems.

Metal Stamping A process of forming, trimming, embossing, flanging, or piercing a piece of steel sheet metal with a metal die (a tool that cuts or presses a shape into the metal it is cutting or forming). For more, see "Precision Metal Stamping".

Metallurgy A science and technique of working with or heating metals to form them into certain desired shapes or properties.

Metal A chemical element that, in general, is a good conductor of heat and electricity.

MRPII (Manufacturing Resource Planning II) A computer system that integrates production planning and control information with other business information, such as customer, personnel, engineering, accounting, and finance.

Net Present Value of Future Cash Flow A calculation that shows the current worth of a future stream of cash flow given a specified rate of return on investment. It is used to determine whether a particular investment will yield a satisfactory return if capital is invested.

North American Free Trade Agreement (NAFTA) A trade agreement signed by Canada, Mexico, and the United States that went into effect on January 1, 1994, to form a North American trading region. In early October 2018 the U.S., Mexico, and Canada revised NAFTA. The new trade agreement is known as the United States-Mexico-Canada Agreement, or USMCA.

Numerical Control (NC) A form of programmable automation in which a machines processes are controlled by a computer program, which is embedded with instructions so that the end product will meet the desired design.

Operations Engineering A branch of engineering concerned with the analysis and optimization of solving operational problems, such as poor quality issues or inefficient production operations.

Payback Period A length of time required for an investment to recover its initial expenditure of capital (money) in terms of profits or savings.

pH Stainless Steel A precipitation-hardened, corrosion-resistant stainless steel that contains the elements chromium and nickel. Precipitation hardening is a heat treatment technique used to increase the strength of materials. Parts made out of this type of stainless steel are commonly used in aerospace applications, chemical processing equipment, oil and petroleum refining equipment, nuclear applications, and other applications where a component needs to have high strength and be corrosion-resistant.

Plastic A man-made substance made from any number of organic, synthetic, or processed materials. Many plastics begin with the prefix "poly" (meaning "many" or "multi"), such as polyethylene, polystyrene, and polypropylene.

Plastic Injection Molding A method of forming plastic pieces by heating the plastic molding material until it can flow, and then injecting that melted plastic into a mold to make a desired form.

Plastic Stamping A manufacturing method that uses a high-speed punch press with tooling and dies that enable a shape to be punched out of a strip of plastic.

Powder Coating A dry finishing process that is harder and more durable than liquid paint. Powder coatings are resistant to impact, moisture, chemicals, ultraviolet light, and extreme weather conditions, which makes them scratch, chip, abrasion, and corrosion resistant. Powder coating is available in an almost limitless range of textures and colors.

Precision Hard-Chrome Plating A chromic acid-based coating put on metals that is corrosion-resistant and has a low coefficient of friction ("drag").

Precision Machining A process to remove material, such as from a chunk or round bar of metal or plastic, to make a desired shape, while maintaining close tolerance finishes to the "thousandth" or "ten-thousandth" of an inch measurement (e.g., +/- .001" or +/- .0001"). What does .001" look like? If you take a ruler and divide it into 1,000 pieces, each of those pieces equals one-thousandth of an inch (.001"). Here's another example: A piece of human hair is .002" in diameter (round). If you split a human hair into 100 pieces, each of those pieces will be .0002" in size. Precision machines are usually controlled by computers (see "CNC Precision Machining").

Precision Metal Stamping A process of converting a flat piece of metal into various shapes by using a tool and die surface. Common metal stamping operations are piercing, bending, embossing, and progressive stamping, where multiple dies are used to make a part (see "Progressive Die Process").

Precision Slide-Forming A metal stamping process that combines with the progressive die process, which consists of several individual work-stations, each of which perform one or more different operations on the part. Producing components in this way allows multiple cutting and/or forming operations to occur simultaneously.

Production A process of combining various materials, blueprints/plans, processes, and know-how (known as "inputs") in order to make products for consumers (individuals, businesses, governments, etc.) to use and/or consume (known as "outputs"). Production is the act of creating output, whether a good or a service, that has value and contributes usefulness to individuals.

Purchasing A department in an organization responsible for acquiring goods or services to operate the business and enable the organization to produce the products and services it sells to customers. Examples of goods purchased by a manufacturing business are raw materials such as metal, plastic, wood, cotton, ingredients to make food products, office supplies, water and oil-based lubricants, tooling, and more.

Quality Control (QC) A procedure, or set of procedures, documented and carried out by workers to ensure that a manufactured product meets the quality criteria specified by the customer.

Quality Control Inspectors A person that ensures the product and process standards set by the company are maintained, and also those of the state and/or federal government, as applicable.

Robotics A branch of engineering that involves the conception, design, manufacture, and operation of robots.

Screw Machine A small to medium-sized automatic lathe with machines parts that either are (or need to be) round, such as screws and valves. These machines were first developed in Switzerland during the late 1800s to produce large numbers of identical parts, namely, metal screws.

Secondary Machine (or Second-Op Machine) A machine used to perform operations that weren't done in the primary process. Secondary machines perform operations such as drilling, reaming, tapping, and slotting.

Server A computerized process that can be used or called upon by another process (particularly remotely). Any general-purpose computer connected to a network can host servers.

Shop Floor A term used in to tell where assembly or production operations take place. The shop floor may house machinery, tooling, and inventory storage areas.

STEM A series of educational topics that prepares primary and secondary students for careers, and college, in the fields of science, technology, engineering, and mathematics.

Swiss Turning A specialized process performed on a Swiss-style lathe for machining small, high-precision turned parts, such as medical components. A Swiss machine deflects and vibrates less than a traditional CNC lathe because of the use of a guide bushing, a holding mechanism that is placed in front of the collet. A guide bushing offers additional support to the stock material while it is being machined or turned.

Tooling A term used to refer to different types of cutting tool (such as drills), gauges (to measure sizes and tolerances), molds (forms that shape material), dies (pieces that cut or shape material, usually via a press, such as in stamping), and fixtures (which hold the material being worked on in a fixed location).

Toolmaker A machinist who specializes in the construction, repair, maintenance, and calibration of the tools, jigs, fixtures, and other instruments used in a machine shop.

Acknowledgements

Thank you to all the individuals who contributed their ideas, inspiration, and examples as I authored this book. These people include Patricia Squier, Janet Kaiser, Erica Wiegel, Patricia Miller, Debbie Sommers, Kim Beal, Emily Mitchell, Cassie Sommers, Stephanie Suerth, MaryJo Lanz, Tonya Reyes, Rich Hoster, Renee Schroeder, Cynthia Campos, Stacia Hobson, Nicole Wolter, and Marisol Comacha.

Thank you to my father, Gerald E. Troutman, for being the most influential person in my life and the best father a daughter could ever have. I miss your kind, gentle nature, your brilliance—you. Your voice is missed, but your legacy lives on.

Thank you to my uncle, David G. Troutman, who took the time to share rich, colorful stories about the Troutman family history, my father, and the early days when he started his business, Troutman Machine Shop. His stories made our family business story come to life.

Thank you to my husband, Robert, who gave me the time and support I needed to author this book, and for being the one who creates the adventure in our lives.

Thank you to my son, Michael, and my daughters, Janelle and Rebecca, who provide me with the deepest meaning and purpose in my life. They are why I do all I do and have done in my life.

Thank you to my developmental copy editor and book writing coach, Christine Thom, for helping me shape my ideas and offer advice at many steps along the way, and encouraging me—rather *pushed* me—

to write in a way so that my authentic voice was rendered, and my story was told to honor the memory, and legacy of my father. She is a creative and generous thought partner, guide, and friend.

Thank you to my copy editor and proofreader, Lauren Slawson, for helping to refine, and polish this book, making it shine even brighter. She provided expert advice, ideas, and encouragement to me that this book delivers a worthy, and important message to young women.

Thank you to my friends, and colleagues, Denise Hansard and Beth Marshall, for giving me the encouragement to listen to my heart's gentle guidance while writing this book, breathing life into the stories within.

Share This Exciting Story

Do you want to help more young women learn about exciting and fulfilling job and career growth opportunities in the manufacturing industry, a STEM-related field? For more information visit my website:

Profit-Strategies.com/WomenWhoMakeBook

Notes

1. Eric Morath and Andrew Van Dam, "Where Are the Most U.S. Manufacturing Workers? Los Angeles," *The Wall Street Journal,* July 15, 2015, 4:50 p.m. ET, https://blogs.wsj.com/economics/2015/07/15/where-are-the-most-u-s-manufacturing-workers-los-angeles/.

2. Jordon, "Why is manufacturing important?", The Global Teach-In, April 15, 2012. www.globalteachin.com/articles/why-is-manufacturing-important.

3. Steve Lohr, "Where the STEM Jobs Are (and Where They Aren't)," *New York Times,* November 1, 2017, https://www.nytimes.com/2017/11/01/education/edlife/stem-jobs-industry-careers.html.

4. "Women in manufacturing: Stepping up to make an impact that matters," Deloitte, accessed August 28, 2018, https://www2.deloitte.com/us/en/pages/manufacturing/articles/women-in-manufacturing-industrial-products-and-services.html. An analysis of the survey conducted by the Manufacturing Institute, APICS, and Deloitte. See also: "Degrees conferred by postsecondary institutions, by level of degree and sex of student: Selected years, 1869–70 through 2025–26," National Center for Education Statistics, table 318.10, accessed November 6, 2018, https://nces.ed.gov/programs/digest/d15/tables/dt15_318.10.asp.

5. Anna Powers, "A Stanford Study Offers Insights As To Why There Are So Few Women In Stem," *Forbes,* September 30, 2018, 110:00 a.m., https://www.forbes.com/sites/annapowers/2018/09/30/a-stanford-study-offers-insights-as-to-why-there-are-so-few-women-in-stem/#690efca8614b.

6. Nicole Skibola, "The Immeasurable Value of Retaining Women in the Workplace," *Forbes,* December 2, 2010, 10:43 a.m., https://www.forbes.com/sites/csr/2010/12/02/the-immeasurable-value-of-retaining-women-in-the-workplace/#21983bae7d34.

7. "The STEM Imperative," Smithsonian Science Education Center, accessed January 28, 2019, https://ssec.si.edu/stem-imperative.

8. Farran Powell, "What You Need to Know About College Tuition Costs," *U.S. News and World Report,* updated September 19, 2018, https://www.usnews.com/education/best-colleges/paying-for-college/articles/what-you-need-to-know-about-college-tuition-costs.

9. "A Look at the Shocking Student Loan Debt Statistics for 2018," Student Loan Hero, updated February 4, 2019, https://studentloanhero.com/student-loan-debt-statistics/.
10. Ken Robinson, "Changing education paradigms." October 2010. TED, RSA Animate video. https://www.ted.com/talks/ken_robinson_changing_education_paradigms.
11. "Graduation Rates," Fast Facts, National Center for Education Statistics, November 28, 2018, https://nces.ed.gov/fastfacts/display.asp?id=40.
12. David A. Tomar, "Trade Schools On the Rise," The Quad, accessed November 28, 2018, https://thebestschools.org/magazine/trade-schools-rise-ashes-college-degree.
13. Trevor English, "Top Reasons Why the U.S. Manufacturing Industry is Growing," Inventor Blog, Autodesk, February 7, 2017, http://blogs.autodesk.com/inventor/2017/02/07/top-reasons-u-s-manufacturing-industry-growing/.
14. "The Top 18 Facts You Need to Know," Facts About Manufacturing, National Association of Manufacturers, accessed December 10, 2018, https://www.nam.org/Newsroom/Top-20-Facts-About-Manufacturing/.
15. Ibid.
16. Ibid.
17. Ibid.
18. Ibid.
19. "Table 322.20. Bachelor's degrees conferred by postsecondary institutions, by race/ethnicity and sex of student: Selected years, 1976-77 through 2015-16," National Center for Education Statistics, accessed January 29, 2019, https://nces.ed.gov/programs/digest/d17/tables/dt17_322.20.asp.
20. "Historical Marital Status Tables, Table MS-2. Estimated Median Age First Marriage, by Sex: 1890 to the Present," United States Census Bureau, accessed January 29, 2019, https://www.census.gov/data/tables/time-series/demo/families/marital.html.
21. "Second-wave feminism," Khan Academy, accessed March 2, 2019, https://www.khanacademy.org/humanities/us-history/postwarera/1960s-america/a/second-wave-feminism.
22. "Historical Marital Status Tables," United States Census Bureau, [insert table number], accessed January 29, 2019, https://www.census.gov/data/tables/time-series/demo/families/marital.html.
23. Gretchen Livingston, "They're Waiting Longer, but U.S. Women Today More Likely to Have Children Than a Decade Ago," Pew Research Center, Social and Demographic Trends, January 18, 2018,

http://www.pewsocialtrends.org/2018/01/18/theyre-waiting-longer-but-u-s-women-today-more-likely-to-have-children-than-a-decade-ago.
24. "History of the Wyomissing Polytechnic Institute," Penn State Berks, accessed December 31, 2018, https://berks.psu.edu/history-wyomissing-polytechnic-institute.
25. Erin Negley, "Made in Berks: Quadrant squeezes profits out of plastic," Reading Eagle, accessed September 3, 2014, https://www.readingeagle.com/business-weekly/article/made-in-berks-quadrant-squeezes-profits-out-of-plastic.
26. Kimberly Amadeo, "History of Recessions in the United States; Causes, Length, GDP, and Unemployment Rates," The Balance, last updated June 6, 2019, https://www.thebalance.com/the-history-of-recessions-in-the-united-states-3306011.
27. Ibid.
28. Ibid.
29. "Boscov's Department Store, Inc.," Company-Histories.com, accessed January 5, 2019, http://www.company-histories.com/Boscovs-Department-Store-Inc-Company-History.html.
30. "Machine Tool Technology, AAS," Reading Area Community College, accessed June 28, 2019, http://catalog.racc.edu/preview_program.php?catoid=11&poid=1400&returnto=406.
31. "W. Kent Kise, Jr.," DeBord Snyder Funeral Home & Crematory, Inc., accessed January 5, 2019, https://www.debordsnyder.com/w-kent-kise-jr/.
32. Bionic Disco, "Enjoli Perfume 'I'm A Woman' Commercial (1979)," *YouTube* video, 13:59. March 5, 2019. https://www.youtube.com/watch?v=N_kzJ-f5C9U.
33. Philip H. Dougherty, "Archives," *New York Times*, October 31, 1979, https://www.nytimes.com/1979/10/31/archives/advertising-secrets-of-selling-to-women.html.
34. "Cited Stats," Family Business Alliance, updated December 11, 2018, www.fbagr.org/resources/cited-stats/, as cited in "Family Business Facts," Conway Center for Family Business, accessed September 15, 2018, https://www.familybusinesscenter.com/resources/family-business-facts/.

About the Author

Bonita Richter, MBA, is the president of the executive consulting firm Profit Strategies. Their clients include top-tier, and mid-market organizations. She is known for her ability to shed light on the business problems that are hiding in plain sight and executing solutions with precision with her practical, straightforward style.

Richter previously served as a finance executive in her family-owned, CNC precision machining manufacturing firm, and as the director of a business development center at a community college. She is a graduate of the Pennsylvania State University and the Lake Forest Graduate School of Management. She is currently a faculty member at the Lake Forest Graduate School of Management where she prepares MBA candidates for success by helping them to develop their leadership and business management skills.

Made in the USA
Middletown, DE
11 November 2021

52157327R00102